Biog

W9-ADS-471

STAR OF JACOB

"Balaam the son of Beor, the man whose eyes are open, has said: I shall see him, but not now: I shall behold him, but not nigh: there shall come a star out of Jacob, and a sceptre shall rise out of Israel" (Num. 24:17).

"Behold there came wise men from the east to Jerusalem, saying, Where is he that is born king of the Jews? for we have seen his star in the east, and are come to adore him" (Matt. 2:2).

THE VENERABLE FRANCIS LIBERMANN BY CARL SCHMITT

Star of Jacob

The Story of
the Venerable Francis Libermann

FOUNDER OF THE CONGREGATION OF THE HOLY GHOST
AND OF THE IMMACULATE HEART OF MARY

By Helen Walker Homan

DAVID McKAY COMPANY, INC., NEW YORK

CARMELITE MONASTERY
68 FRANKLIN AVENUE
SARANAC LAKE, NEW YORK

COPYRIGHT, 1953, BY

HOLY GHOST FATHERS

FERNDALE, NORWALK, CONNECTICUT

All rights reserved, including the right to reproduce this book, or portions thereof, in any form, except for the inclusion of brief quotations in a review.

Fifth Printing

NIHIL OBSTAT:

FRANCIS H. MCGLYNN, C.S.SP.

CENSOR DEPUTATUS

IMPRIMATUR:

✠ HENRY J. O'BRIEN

BISHOP OF HARTFORD

AUGUST 12, 1953

Library of Congress Catalog Card Number: 53-11370

MANUFACTURED IN THE UNITED STATES OF AMERICA

To

THE SONS OF FATHER LIBERMANN,

of

yesterday, today, and tomorrow—
far flung in their glory,
eternal in their destiny.

Foreword

On the first day of July of the year 1876, Rome bestowed the title, "The Venerable Servant of God," upon a man who had ever regarded himself as the least of the servants of God. He had died in Paris but a scant twenty-five years earlier. The son of a devout and scholarly rabbi in Alsace—the Rabbi of Saverne—he was a founder of one of the greatest missionary societies of the Catholic Church: the Congregation of the Holy Ghost and of the Immaculate Heart of Mary.

To Rome, those who had known him gave eloquent testimony to his sanctity, and the process of his beatification was begun. The vivid personality, the alert intellect, the genius for leadership, and the boundless charity which had made him beloved by many—Alsatians, French, Germans, Italians, Americans, Africans—seemed still vibrant in their midst. From the day of his death, they had appealed to him as though he were still among them. And they believed that he responded with open hands and open heart, as he had when upon earth. A multitude of voices was raised in petition, asking Rome to proclaim the sanctity that had been a benediction among them.

Brought up in strict conformity to the Old Law, he had come to embrace the New, understanding it not as a severance, but as a continuity and a fulfillment—the wondrous blossoming of the Israel of old. His spirit moved easily across the eternal bridge that links the two.

Death, and the hundred years which have followed, have only increased the number of his friends. In the following pages one of the least of these has attempted to tell his story, overwhelmed at times by the inadequacies of a pen unworthy of it. But it is the writer's hope that devotion may serve to soften imperfection, and that those who read these pages will understand what she has tried to do.

The span of time has also seen the roots, which he planted with firmness and vision, grow and send heavenward the branches of a great tree. They have spread across many lands, sheltering and nourishing the poor and the abandoned. In Africa alone, the seat of his congregation's first major missionary effort, more than a thousand Holy Ghost Fathers have laid down their lives in dispensing the charity of Christ. Mauritius, Haiti, the Island of Bourbon—the Rodriguez Islands, Martinique, Réunion, Trinidad, Guadeloupe, Amazonia, and Madagascar—have witnessed their labors.

The tree spread out from its motherhouse in France and set its roots down in Ireland, Germany, Portugal, Belgium, Holland, Canada, England, Poland, and Switzerland, whose provinces have sent a multitude of missioners to the world's needy and neglected areas. In 1873, the United States province was established in a small novitiate in Arkansas. It now functions in six archdioceses and twenty dioceses. Duquesne University in Pittsburgh was founded by the American province in 1878. Professed members of the congregation today number more than five thousand. In the mission territories entrusted to them, they minister to upward of twenty-five million souls.

On June 19, 1910, the Vatican, in the presence of Pope Pius X, acknowledged the Venerable founder's heroicity of virtues.

Throughout the congregation's history, his spirit has permeated its endeavors and inspired the heroic labors of his sons. Today, as a hundred years ago, he points the way to that peace which the world cannot give—peace with God and man.

It is this spirit, made vocal in his letters and spiritual counsels, and gleaming like a thread of gold in the tapestry of a brief lifetime of but fifty years, which has more than once challenged the biographer's pen. And it is this spirit which has led the writer to attempt to reconstruct his story in semi-fictionalized form—observing historical accuracy as far as possible in the principal facts, dates, and personalities. Much is owed to the earlier biographers: to Goepfert, to Lee; to Doering and Noppinger; and to Briault who condensed the valuable work of Cabon—all of whom have perpetuated the glory of a great soul.

For the psychological aspects of Father Libermann's malady the writer is indebted to the scholarship of a friend who chooses to remain nameless; and for the physiological aspects to Dr. Justin L. Greene of the New York Neurological Institute.

The writer expresses gratitude also to the friends who have given generously in counsel to the ensuing pages: to certain distinguished members of the Holy Ghost Fathers in this country; to Miss Julie Kernan, Mrs. Justin L. Greene, and Mr. Charles Rich.

Together we join in an expression of gratitude to the founder himself—the Venerable Francis Marie Paul Libermann, born Jacob Libermann on a day in Saverne in the year 1802—whose star continues to lead increasing numbers to the feet of God.

HELEN WALKER HOMAN

New York
Feast of St. Peter and St. Paul
June 29, 1953

Contents

STAR OF JACOB

CHAPTER ONE

The Dream

THE DEAD HAD BEEN decently interred in the little cemetery high up on the hill on that fair day of April in the year 1807. Slowly the procession wound its way down the Alsatian hillside, the somberly garbed mourners following the parish priest, before whom walked an acolyte. The white-haired priest, in surplice and stole, trod a measured pace. Under the dancing sun of the spring morning, the large brass crucifix, held high in the acolyte's hands, became a bright and shining beacon behind which decorously moved the dark procession.

As it reached the foot of the hill and turned toward the town of Saverne, a small boy suddenly emerged from the woodland a few paces ahead of it, coming almost face to face with the crucifix. For the space of a breath he paused and crouched like a terrified rabbit; then in an instant was gone as though propelled headlong by some strong invisible hand. The thick bushes along the country roadside gave no perceptible sign of his quick trespass, so slight was the impact made

1

by the small figure. The crucifix had not wavered in the hands of the acolyte, nor had the parish priest, head bent in prayer, seemed to notice.

A scant few moments later on a narrow street flanking the market place of Saverne, Isaac the baker looked up startled from his freshly baked loaves as the door of his shop burst open and young Jacob Libermann, the son of the Rabbi, dashed white-faced and palpitating beneath the counter, almost knocking the stout baker from his feet.

"The goyim, the goyim!" panted the cowering lad.

"Come, come, Shaekle," admonished the baker, using the endearing diminutive "little Jacob," as he lifted the boy up and sat him gently upon the counter. "No one can hurt you here. Tell Isaac what has happened."

Tears of fright glistened in the big, velvety brown eyes; one or two had trickled to the tender, olive-skinned cheeks, and Jacob was applying a grubby fist to a small nose.

"They came down the hill . . . I was playing huntsman-in-the-forest . . . they came at me, the goyim . . . they raised their fearful sign and tried to strike me with it."

"No, no, Shaekle. You only thought that. Today there was a funeral. The widow Zimmerhof is dead. The goyim always carry their sign at funerals. You will have to get used to seeing it carried through the streets of Saverne."

"Father said I was never to look upon it—that I would be cursed forever—that it is the sign of evil."

"Your father, our holy Rabbi, is a very learned man," began Isaac, tentatively. Little Jacob looked up through his tears:

"He knows everything," he said simply.

"But he only meant you were not to *follow* their sign."

"Their rabbi," went on the still frightened boy, "he—"

"Their priest, you mean," corrected Isaac. "Why, the old curé wouldn't hurt anybody."

"He was with them. He wore those things about his neck! Father says that he has some evil spell and is just waiting to cast it on little Jewish boys."

"He won't bother you if you leave him alone," said Isaac, smoothing the boy's rumpled hair. "Here's a nice fresh bun for you. Get your mother to put some cheese on it. It's good!"

Jacob, holding Isaac's huge hand still dusted with flour, trotted at his side to the door.

"How old are you, Shaekle?"

"I am all of five," came the proud answer.

"Well now, you're growing up and must begin to act like a grown-up, and not be so easily frightened."

"Yes, Isaac." The boy rubbed vigorously at the telltale tears. "I'll try. Thank you for the bun. I'll run all the way home so I can eat it while it's still hot."

"Do," called the baker as the small figure vanished in the direction of the market place of Saverne.

Traversing at an angle the market place with its worn stones and figures of ancient forgotten heroes, the youngster's running feet carried him into a narrow, winding street which led toward the canal. On the way he passed full-skirted peasant women in bob-cap and kerchief, carrying baskets of farm produce; and peddlers of his own race who gave him friendly greeting. The banker, Schwarz, who regularly attended synagogue, was just entering his countinghouse and hailed him affectionately: "Ah, Shaekle, the early bird!" Two distinguished gentlemen, clad in the lastest Empire fashion—smartly cut, tight-fitting garments of rich black, relieved by snowy stocks—smiled at him from the morning stagecoach as it rolled past. They would be goyim, thought Jacob, casting down his eyes. Such travelers might be from Metz or Strasbourg—or even from Paris, his father had told him. Although the boy was unaware of it, the coach also carried within its depths a dark, bearded figure now bent upon a visit to the Libermann home.

As the lad neared the house of the Rabbi, he paused for a moment, putting the precious bun in his pocket. The older brothers might see it—they were Samson, David, Henoch, and Felkel. Samson, twelve years older than he, could be trusted. But the others constantly made sport of him and took from him anything he treasured—that is, when their mother was not looking. Samuel, who was younger, and the little baby sister Esther posed no threat, but were the endearing objects of his love.

At the door stood his mother, her morning apron widespread as though to catch an escaping chick.

"Shaekle, my turtledove, where have you been? Stealing out that way, in the early morning, and without breakfast. What will your father say?" And then, before the breathless boy could answer: "I shall not tell him."

"Mother mine," came the muffled voice from the small head buried in her apron, "please don't tell. I woke up . . . and then I ran to the woods to play at hunting. And then—and then—I came upon the Evil One—the chief of the goyim! It was terrible! Father would surely beat me. Don't tell!"

"Now, now," soothed his mother, "surely he did not hurt you, Shaekle?"

"No—for I ran as fast as I could, to Isaac's; and hid under the counter. And he gave me a fresh bun, and said you should put a morsel of cheese on it." He drew the bun tenderly from his pocket. "But please, not when my brothers are looking."

Léa Suzanne, of the respectable Jewish family of Haller and wife of the Rabbi of Saverne, gathered the boy into her arms. Of all the seven, this was her dearest—although she would rather have perished than admit it. Little Jacob was so appealing—there was something about him. Then too, he had suffered—such a tiny mite to suffer! The others had all been strong. But Léa remembered how when Jacob was scarcely a year old she had sat up night after night by his cradle while a strange fever burned the small body as though in a fierce desire to consume it. Her tears of fright and compassion had mingled with the cool water of the compresses the doctor had ordered. Since then, he had never been really strong; she had nursed him through more illnesses than she cared to remember. Vividly to her mind came the doctor's words: "This baby is different. You must take greater care. He has not the strength of the others." Léa had taken greater care—and accordingly loved in greater measure.

"The cheese shall be yours, my lambkin," she said, hurrying him into the kitchen. "And a big cup of fresh milk as well. Now eat quietly and slowly. The big boys have gone to school; little Samuel is playing with his blocks; the baby has been fed and is sleeping; and your father is busy in his study with a visitor from Metz."

Jacob, perched on a stool, watched his mother as she spread the cheese and poured out the cold milk. How pretty was his mother! She had thick, red-gold hair—an unusual beauty which had distinguished her from the other dusky-haired Jewish maidens of her girlhood. She wore it in glossy braids coiled high upon the top of her head. Beneath them, her large soft brown eyes looked out upon the world with both courage and disarming gentleness. Her skin was as smooth as the cream she always ladled into the *schäve*, the soup which she prepared on the eve of every Sabbath. To be sure, thought Jacob, she was plump—but that went along with mothers.

"Your father is talking with the Rabbi Scholom," Léa was saying. "He has come all the way from Metz to consult your father about a passage in the Torah." The last word was spoken with reverence.

"Who is the Rabbi Scholom?" asked Jacob between munches.

"Why, don't you remember? No, of course you wouldn't. You weren't yet born when he came to Saverne to study; and you were only a tiny babe when he left. He was here a long time, and we accepted him as our own son, while your father instructed him in the Jewish law and the Prophets. Now he himself is a rabbi in Metz, where he is a credit to all he learned in this house, and a light to the Jewish people."

Just then Jacob heard the creaking of the study door. Then came his father's voice; one of authority and yet somehow melodic.

"Léa, send Jacob to the study at once!"

The creaking door closed. Sliding from the stool almost before Léa could wipe the crumbs from the small face, Jacob was off in a flash. At the study door he paused a moment, trying to steady a pair of shaking knees. Did his father know of the early morning adventure? Then resolutely he put his knuckles to the door and rapped.

The Rabbi's study had always been a place of fascination for Jacob. While the house was a small, two-storied affair, with an overhanging high gabled roof such as you might see pictured in a fairy story and a narrow façade showing but three windows above and two below, it stretched far enough to the rear to permit bedroom space for the family of nine and yet provide the Rabbi with his own workroom on the first floor. Books were everywhere—on the walls, on the commodious desk, and on a table or two—and in a glass-covered case there were displayed three precious scrolls. On a high shelf beyond his reach was a book Jacob particularly loved. It had engravings of great ships and pictured absorbing rescues at sea. When he had worked especially hard at his Psalms and had pleased his father, the Rabbi would take it down and let him look at the pictures as he related the heroic adventures they represented.

As Jacob entered, his father arose from a worn upholstered chair. He was slender and of middling height, with long flowing beard shot with gray, black skullcap astride stubbornly curly hair; and he bore the slightly stooped shoulders and protruding head of the scholar. There was something of the nobility of the eagle in that face, with its piercing eyes and strongly carved nose and chin.

"This is the Rabbi Scholom," he was saying, as he led Jacob to the visitor. "And this, our little Jacob, who was only a baby when you left us. Observe how he has grown!"

Solemnly Jacob took the stranger's hand. He looked up into a face sharply cut in impressive pattern. The protruding dark eyes looked like hard marbles, thought Jacob. And he wondered why the stranger's beard, less luxuriant than his father's, seemed to recede into his chest instead of hanging properly and handsomely from a square chin. When the Rabbi Scholom smiled, Jacob was somehow reminded of the gargoyles on the exterior of one of Saverne's ancient churches. A church of the goyim, Jacob had been sternly told to

avert his glance whenever he passed it. But once, out of terrified curiosity, he had cast "side-eyes" as he lagged behind his
father who was bent on an errand of charity to a poor Jewish
family. Then he had observed the grimacing gargoyles which
had both repelled and attracted him. Rabbi Scholom was now
smiling in the same way. Bending over the boy, he said:

"Ah, Shaekle, you have truly grown! And how soon will
you start your schooling?"

"Father is already teaching me," answered Jacob proudly.
"And soon I shall begin the classes in the school my big
brothers attend."

"I'm starting the boy right, as I started the others," said
Rabbi Libermann. "He must learn Hebrew first; and early to
memorize parts of the Law, and the Prophets. My sons, I
hope, will all follow their father's path, so that one day, my
friend, you may know, not *one* Rabbi Libermann, but also
six others!"

Scholom stroked his beard and nodded in approval.

"That is as it should be, my teacher. The God of our Fathers
has seen fit to bless your marriage with a goodly flock. Ah,
our woe is deep that my Rita and I still remain childless."

"You are yet young," observed the older man. "You must
not cease your prayers to the All-Powerful to fructify your
marriage."

"True." And then as though to change the topic, the visitor
turned awkwardly to Jacob.

"And where will our young Jacob go for study when he is
ready to be sent forth?"

The older Rabbi beamed. "This son," he said, "must have
the best. His older brothers are quick at their studies, but for
his age, this one surpasses them all, except perhaps Samson,

my eldest." He took Jacob's hand in his, and with slow emphasis continued, "Already at five, he has memorized whole passages from the Psalms. He is never happier than when he is with me here, listening as I read the Law, and interpret. Is it not so, my Shaekle?"

The boy's heart danced within him. Smilingly, he nodded his head. "Yes, my father."

"And so," the Rabbi continued, "he must have the best of training." He paused impressively. And then:

"Should it please the Lord of Israel," he continued, "and should you, Scholom, my beloved pupil, not object, I plan to send him first to you, in Metz; when he is perhaps twenty—even as you came to me at that age."

Scholom blinked rapidly and then showed his smile at its widest. Bowing slightly, he said:

"You do me great honor, my teacher. I will indeed welcome Jacob with fatherly arms when that bright day shall come. He shall be to me, as I was to you, a son. How will you like that, my young Jacob, eh?"

Jacob backed away from the dark figure bending over him. He hung his head, and silently traced a pattern on the worn carpet with his toe.

"Come, Jacob," said his father sharply, "give a civil answer to the kind Rabbi Scholom."

There were tears in the boy's eyes as he looked up adoringly at his father.

"I want to stay with you—forever and ever," he said simply.

The stern expression on the father's face relaxed into a smile. Playfully he tousled the small head.

"And so you shall stay with me—for a long, long time," he promised. "But suppose you should change your mind when

you are a young man, and should desire to see something of
the world? Then, would it not be sad, if the Rabbi Scholom
should also change his mind, and no longer wish to teach
you?"

"I shall always wish to remain with you," replied the boy
stubbornly.

Libermann turned to his friend apologetically.

"He is yet so young: you will understand."

"But it is only natural." The smile appeared widely again.

"You may go now, Jacob," said his father, "but return at
eleven to memorize your new Psalm. Not a minute late, remember."

It had been quite a day already, reflected Jacob, seeking
out his mother whose steps could be heard above as she tidied
the rooms. Could much more of excitement happen? He was
very glad his father did not know about his encounter with
the evil goyim. Also, he did not like that Rabbi Scholom. But
he must not say this to anyone. His father would be cross. It
would be a long time before he would be twenty—almost a
life-time—and by then his mother would have persuaded his
father not to send him to Metz. . . . Samson would soon be
home from school. He had promised, the night before, to
bring him a red crayon. He loved Samson. But as soon as the
others saw it, they would take it from him and probably break
it, he reflected soberly. He must find a good hiding place for
it. If he put it under his pillow, would it be crushed? His
mother could tell him. More than once she and he had played
at hiding treasure. Mother was awfully good at thinking of
new places, she was. . . . Yet, she would be very busy today. For tomorrow would be the Sabbath, when no work, no

cooking—nothing—could be done. Except, attend the synagogue, and pray. And pray. . . .

That night, tucked in his bed next to that of the little brother Samuel (Samson and David occupied another room; Henoch and Felkel a third, while the baby sister slept in the room of their parents), the five-year-old Jacob had a dream.

It seemed to him that he was on a vast sea, alone, and in a small boat. A tempest lashed the waters, and he felt certain that his boat would be engulfed, that he would perish in the raging sea. Then suddenly, afar off, he glimpsed a bright and shining light approaching, more gleaming than the brightest star. It must come from a great ship. It would rescue him, he thought. With renewed strength he clung to the sides of his little boat, trying to hold it steady. If only he could keep it upright until those on the great ship would see him!

Gradually the bright light grew larger, approaching nearer and nearer. He strained in vain to see the giant outlines of a ship. But he could see nothing but that bright, almost blinding light, ever growing larger and brighter, ever coming closer, until his first delight at the prospect of being rescued turned to the sheer terror of being engulfed. Then, as he gazed, paralyzed with fear, to his horror he saw a cross in the center of the bright light. Upon the cross there hung limply the figure of a man, white, and dead. So white; so dead. And as the great light moved implacably nearer and nearer, and seemed about to engulf him, he awoke, screaming. . . .

CHAPTER TWO

The Brother

SINCE THE MIDDLE AGES Alsace, in spite of war and vicissitudes, had drawn to it many of the Jewish race. The basic Catholicism of France, the Lutheranism of the Germanic States, and the Judaism of Israel moved elbow to elbow in old Saverne. When Jacob was born on April 12th of the year 1802, Alsace had been a province of France for one hundred and fifty-four years. But the Alsatian tongue lingered on, and one could hear both French and the ancient dialect in a friendly disorder in the market place and streets of the city. Jacob's father, the Rabbi Lazarus Libermann, undisputed leader of the Jewish minority, recognized but one tongue—the ancient Hebrew.

His synagogue stood next door to the house. With its austere façade, its tall narrow doorway arched in the Moorish fashion, and its sharply peaked gabled roof which rose higher than that of the Rabbi's dwelling, it seemed somewhat like a protecting big brother, holding the smaller one close to its side. Nearby, and in the adjoining lanes and streets, lived most of the religious Jews of Saverne, clustered as near as possible to what they regarded as the keystone of their existence.

The two buildings stood on a narrow street, and vis-à-vis the Rabbi's home was an iron railing, waist-high, obviously intended to keep unwary pedestrians from tumbling off into a debased *quai* bordering the Rhine-Marne canal. On the lower level could be seen housewives with baskets of laundry, gathered there to do their weekly washing. The activities along the *quai* were absorbing to the young Jacob, and he spent many hours watching them.

A year had passed since he had first had the frightening dream. It had recurred more than once, but his mother had never failed to answer the frightened cries in the night, and with ancient Jewish lullabies, crooned in her soft contralto voice, had soothed away the nightmare. Recently his oldest brother Samson, now eighteen, had told him that a boy of six who had already started school should not be frightened by dreams, or cry out. He must just lie there bravely in the dark, with his eyes open; and gradually he would see the familiar objects in the room taking shape and realize that it was only a dream, that he was safe at home. It was too bad to frighten the little brother Samuel who slept near him. So Jacob had tried, and the dream was recurring less frequently.

Nowadays, when he awakened in the morning, he would toss the covers aside and leap from bed with a light heart to be the first at the long morning prayer with which his father, every day, solemnly began the family life. "How beautiful are thy tents, O Jacob, and thy dwellings, O Israel. . . ." Then, hastily swallowing his breakfast, he would be out the door to lean over the railing, absorbed in the activities of the *quai*.

There would be a full fascinating hour before it would be time to start for school.

As for the synagogue, he had begun to regard it as his second home. There, on the Sabbath and on holy days, he could observe his father as the powerful leader, be assured of the love and respect in which he was held by all the Jews of Saverne. The young heart opened itself wide to the ancient ceremonials, to the majestic message of the Prophets.

How long must his father have labored to achieve such eminence! He had begun his career as a merchant, but had applied himself so brilliantly to rabbinical studies that eventually he had been chosen by the leaders of the synagogue as their rabbi. Could Jacob himself ever persevere so well, and do as well as his father ardently planned? He sighed as he remembered that it would be seven long years before, at thirteen, he could be accepted as an actual member of the synagogue. He would have to be more than twice his present age before that most important of all the events in a boy's life could take place.

Only a few months before, his brother Henoch had celebrated his *Bar Mitzvah*. Jacob recalled the solemnity, and the suppressed excitement about the house at that time. His father had taken him on his knee and explained that now Henoch was endowed with a new importance. For the first time he would approach the scroll of the Torah, would recite from it and from the Prophets in synagogue, before a large assemblage of grown-ups. Jacob had listened with interest as his father had patiently coached Henoch in the proper intonation of the Hebrew which would be expected on that great occasion. How careful his mother had been to see that

Henoch's fine new suit, of the best quality, should be adjusted perfectly.

Then the great Sabbath had arrived. Jacob had remained spellbound as his brother stood before the large assemblage, the young voice breaking the silence, intoning a beautiful text from the Prophet Ezekiel. When the solemn service was over, there was a great celebration at home—a feast which had been in preparation for days, and was attended by many relatives and friends. . . . Seven more years to wait before Jacob's religious life as a Jew could formally begin! Would they ever pass?

The Rabbi's congregation had almost doubled, he had heard his parents say, during the past ten years. Thriving industries had spread throughout the rich valley. Apart from the ancient wine trade, launched by the Greeks long before the Christian era, there were now flourishing mills in or near the neighborhood which produced linen, cotton, wool, and silk.

The Jewish merchants sold the ribbons and silks to the Christian women for their picturesque native costumes—gay, billowing skirts, snowy blouses of sheerest linen and lace, velvet bodices; and topping all, the great butterfly bows which graced the back of the head and framed a pretty face and glossy hair so becomingly.

Jacob had already learned that there were two types of goyim in Saverne—the type whom the parish priest, with his terrible sign, represented (these were the ones whom his father most distrusted) and others who were only slightly less obnoxious. Maidens of the former lamentable group wore their butterfly bows in red or blue, or any of the gay colors; while maidens of the less dreaded group wore them in sober black. The Jewish women covered their hair completely with dark scarves. They considered as shameless the attire of the other women.

Jacob often wondered why the women of the most dreaded of the goyim, those of the unholy sign, wore the brightly colored bows, seeming to flaunt their gaiety at the dull black of their neighbors. It was as though the former literally rejoiced in their iniquity. He had once asked his father about this, and his father had been inclined to agree with him.

His first months at school had been exciting ones in which he had felt all the ecstasy of a vastly widening world. He found a thrill in the competition with others of his age, but accompanying the thrill there was also an abysmal fear of the schoolmaster. Isaac Mendelbaum, tall, spare, with whitened, balding head, wore gigantic spectacles over obtruding, nearsighted eyes. Jacob had never before observed spectacles at such close range. In shape, they were square, and it was as though the schoolmaster were peering out suspiciously from behind two large square windows. All through the first hour Jacob had stared at them, fascinated—until the schoolmaster had come to him where he sat on a long bench with other newcomers and had rapped him sharply on the knuckles with his ruler, reproving him loudly in a rasping voice for staring. For some time after it had been administered, the blow had stung. From then on, Jacob was very careful not to offend.

Later, there had been a terrible day when one of the "big" boys, a lad of eight, had been caught mimicking the schoolmaster as he stood with his back to the class, writing on the large slate which hung upon the wall. The subject who was being impersonated—not without humor—had wheeled about too suddenly. Ensuing was such a scene of fury as Jacob had never before witnessed. It caused his spine to recede violently against the back of the bench, and his small toes to curl inside his shoes. In some fashion his stomach seemed to have broken loose from its moorings. For the schoolmaster had knocked the offender down, seized him by the ankles, and swung his head violently against the wall. Jacob felt sick all day—even though his brothers had warned him that such scenes were not uncommon. But to witness one was quite a different matter.

Strange, about Schoolmaster Mendelbaum. If he really loved God so much, how then could he sometimes hate little boys so much, Jacob often wondered. For God had made little boys, and so He must be rather fond of them—particularly little Jewish boys who were of His Chosen—His Very Own Chosen. What rapture lay in that thought! The realization that you, unimportant as you might be, were one of the Chosen of the Almighty!

Jacob was not sorry that after a month or two at school the schoolmaster had begun to show a sort of sour preference for him, calling upon him frequently to recite in Hebrew; and once even to intone a short text from the Prophets, as his father had taught him. For several years the schoolmaster had been teaching the Rabbi's sons—Samson, David, Henoch, and Felkel—and, barring Samson, this fifth son, young Jacob, gave the greatest promise. But of all this brood whose training in Hebrew by the learned Lazarus Libermann had begun at an early age, Samson had excelled the others. Therefore, after little Jacob had recited, he would say:

"Not bad. Perhaps if you will study hard enough, you will be able to do as well as Samson did at your age."

Everybody knew that Samson was destined to become a

rabbi like his father. Soon he would be off to Mainz to complete his rabbinical studies under some famous scholars, friends of his father's in that city.

The Rabbi Libermann was pleased at Jacob's progress in school. Affectionately he would rub the boy's black curly hair when he returned with tales of his classroom exploits. Big brother Samson would stand by, smiling, and then would lead the lad off to a corner to help him with the first lessons in "numbers" or geography, or to smooth out some difficulty in reading the unpunctuated Hebrew texts.

One day when his father had been particularly well pleased with the record, he had said:

"This afternoon I am going to visit Banker Schwarz. After you have returned from school, you may accompany me, if you like."

Now Banker Schwarz had a grown son, Karl, who was a friend of Samson's, and it was usually Samson who accompanied the Rabbi on such visits. The banker lived near the market place. It would be a matter of great pride, Jacob thought, to be observed walking through the market place with his father. So through the early school hours his heart sang like a canary within him—only to flutter and falter when the schoolmaster launched into one of his periodic tirades against the goyim.

"I warn you again that their blasphemous sign is a cross, with a dead man nailed to it. They claim that this dead man was our awaited Messiah, whom the Prophets have promised. Such a claim is an offense to the Almighty. Our Messiah, who will bless and save the Chosen Children of God, is yet to come to us. Whoever of you looks upon that cross—or whoever enters a church of the goyim—shall be cursed."

At such moments the memory of the terrifying dream would again overwhelm the boy.

"In the long ago," the schoolmaster was explaining, "those blasphemous goyim took the false prophet down from his cross and buried him. Then secretly, and by night, they opened his tomb and stole the body, burying it again where no one could find it. To make their deceitful work easier—and the blasphemy worse—it was upon a Sabbath. Then, when the day after the Sabbath had dawned, they ran hither and thither, telling about the empty tomb and claiming that the false one had risen from death. A preposterous lie, and one perpetrated to our own time—one by reason of which God's Chosen People have been made to suffer greatly."

All this Jacob had heard many times before. He felt relieved when the schoolmaster paused, and moved to the slate to demonstrate a sum in numbers. But even there the theme was not entirely changed, for Mendelbaum was saying:

"You must always be honest with numbers, and in accounting for money. Except when dealing with the goyim. It is not a sin, but rather a merit, to outwit the enemies of Israel in money, as in all things."

That, too, Jacob had heard before. It did seem rather puzzling. His father—what would he say to this? Would the schoolmaster never leave off and ring the bell on his desk, the signal that school was dismissed?

The first out of the door, the first of the brothers to reach home, he encountered his mother in the hall.

"Wash quickly," she said, "and come to the kitchen for some hot food before you start out with your father. . . . Brush your hair carefully, now," she called after him as he tore up the stairs. "Your father must not be shamed by your appearance before Banker Schwarz!"

Excitedly, Jacob dashed his face with water from the jug. With childish gestures he tried to smooth down the unruly curls. He was going to walk through the market place with his father, the great Rabbi of Saverne! And everybody would be assured again, that this was his, Jacob Libermann's, father.

It was a fine September day, and so they took the higher road which led past dwellings and vineyards separated by rough stone walls which had been laid down by hand. Jacob strode along manfully at his father's side. It was very pleasant to be considered sufficiently grown-up to accompany the Rabbi on important business to bankers, and such. Why, he might even be of some help! He could now add up sums—if the figures were not too large. He was reflecting on this ecstatic possibility as they neared a corner where the road turned sharply, its continuing stretch hidden from view.

"We must quicken our pace," his father was saying, "or we shall be late."

Just then they heard the sound of chanting. Rounding the corner, they saw, coming toward them up the road, a throng of persons led by a figure clad in a long cloak of rich gold brocade. He walked beneath a canopy carried by four men, and he held aloft a golden symbol with a white, round center and sprays of sparkling gold radiating from it—as though he had caught the sun and held it captive in his hands.

"Goyim," said his father.

Instinctively, and in an instant, with one terrified leap Jacob had cleared the wall to their right and was running across the fields with the speed of a sparrow on the wing. The

Rabbi stared after him—not without gratification. He would not call the boy back. Then soberly he himself avoided the advancing procession by turning down an intersecting lane.

Jacob's heart pounded in his ears as he ran. They might pursue him! If only he could find a place where he could hide from them, and get his breath! Skimming over another wall, he found himself before a dim, arched opening and in an instant had slid within its shelter. Inside, it was very dark, he realized—dark and still—and the stone wall against which he leaned, struggling for breath, was cool. Gradually his eyes began to discern a high vaulted roof, outlines and spaces. He crept forward curiously, for the moment forgetting entirely that he had left his father so abruptly, back there on the high-road.

Far off, and at an angle from where he stood, there appeared to be a dim light burning. Both fear and curiosity possessed him. He listened. Not a sound broke the stillness, save his own breathing. It must be that he was alone in this vast, dim place. On he crept. Once he stumbled against something of wood that moved, scraping across the uneven stone floor. He drew back, startled. It seemed to be only a low stool. But why did it have two uprights, connected with a board across the top? He looked up again, and the far-off light flickered and glowed, as though beckoning to him. He moved cautiously toward it.

Now he began to see that it burned before an enclosure in the center of which stood an elaborately carved table of stone. There was a small boxlike structure in the center of the table. Raising his eyes, he suddenly caught his breath. There, in naked agony, hung the dead man upon the cross. Jacob stared spellbound, unable to move in his fright. Then a strange thing happened. Suddenly the shaking limbs were stilled, his heart stopped its violent beating, and a sort of peace entered upon him—strange, sweet. He stood there, gazing at the figure on the cross for a long minute, then turned quietly and slipped like a shadow down the central aisle of the church.

Not a moment too soon did he reach the low-vaulted door at the side by which he had entered, for now he heard the big center doors flung wide, and, turning for a last glimpse, saw the enclosure where the lamp hung, now aglow with candle-light; and somewhere off in the distance he heard the rich tones of an organ. Slipping through the arched doorway and peering around the side of the structure, he saw the solemn procession which had put him to flight entering through the main doorway. But he was no longer afraid.

The church he now recognized as that whose ancient, exterior figures had fascinated him—particularly the carved faces high up on the abutments whose stony grimaces again reminded him forcibly of the Rabbi Scholom. And suddenly he knew that he must never tell anyone that he had entered it. For to enter a church of the goyim was blasphemy of the gravest. To be sure, he had not known.

Quietly he walked home, arriving before his father had returned from the visit to Banker Schwarz. Later, the Rabbi did not reprove him for his sudden disappearance.

"Shaekle should know that he is always safe, when he is with me," was all he said.

"Yes, Father," said Jacob, looking up at him trustingly.

During these days when the world was ever opening wider to his astonished gaze, it seemed that adventure awaited him at every turn. One morning when he and Henoch and Felkel were on their way to school—David was already a student in the higher school—they noticed a little knot of persons gathered at the roadside. Pausing curiously, they heard a woman say that a man had been thrown from his horse and was in great pain; that someone had gone for a doctor. As they pushed forward with the other youngsters, they could see the victim stretched out on the grass where compassionate hands had laid him, and someone observed that his leg seemed to be badly injured. As low moans came from the prostrate form, Jacob's eyes grew moist. He wished desperately to help him.

Suddenly there was a stir in the crowd, and everyone stood aside respectfully for the doctor to pass. Felkel plucked at Jacob's sleeve.

"Look," he whispered, "Samson is with him—with the doctor!"

To Jacob's amazement he saw his big brother following closely in the doctor's wake, saw him take off his coat, roll it, and put it gently under the injured man's head, while the doctor bent over the moaning form. Now Samson was opening the doctor's black satchel—was handing him bandages and what appeared to be two or three small flat wooden boards. Jacob could not quite see what the doctor was doing to the man's leg, and could only catch an occasional glimpse as the crowd shifted back and forth. But he saw that Samson was watching the doctor attentively. And suddenly, he was very proud of Samson.

Felkel was again tugging at his sleeve.

"We must go," he whispered. "We'll be late and old Mendelbaum will be awfully cross. He may even fling us against the wall!"

Henoch was already running toward the schoolhouse. Felkel and Jacob sprinted after him. . . .

Now the harvest moon was high, and the air carried a magic elixir that made one want to run and jump and laugh. Golden fall flowers nodded and smiled from the trim gardens, and the great trees on the rugged slopes of the mountains flung out their gorgeous banners of crimson and yellow. Everywhere there was perfume—perfume of apples, perfume of wood-smoke, above all, perfume of the grape. For now the harvest was at full tide; the time had come to cut the grapes, to put them through the wine presses. To some of the larger wine centers lying off in the foothills, which could proudly trace their lineage as far back as the seventh and eighth centuries, peasants had converged from all over the countryside to help with the harvest. They labored from dawn to dark, singing at their tasks, and they danced far into the night.

Samson had heard that a harvest festival was to be held at one of the centers when all the grapes had been gathered. There would be a full day and a night of merrymaking, and all of youthful Saverne had been invited. It would be held on the day preceding his departure for Mainz, for which preparations had long been in progress. His father had written the last letter to all the good friends in Mainz, commending his eldest son to their care and instruction; and his mother had washed and mended his clothes and packed them with care in the large box, along with his new suit—to purchase which had required some skillful economic maneuvering on the part of Léa.

Léa, busy from morning till night with her brood of seven, had been unusually silent of late. Samson, her eldest—he of the quiet sympathy who had always been so stalwart at her side, almost a second father to the children—Samson was leaving the nest. The heart was heavy within her as she contemplated the long years without him. Soon, all too soon, the others would be following him, one by one. Even little Jacob, her own Shaekle; and after him, Samuel. It was comforting to reflect that Esther was a girl, and would not leave home until she married. Léa could not help hoping that such a day would be long postponed.

Samson understood all that was going on within his mother's heart and tried in a thousand unobtrusive ways to comfort her by lightening her burdens, or by cheerful talk. On this particular day he noticed that she seemed especially tired and discouraged. If he could take the youngsters off her hands for a few hours after school, she might have time for a little rest. Therefore, and not without trepidation for all his eighteen years, he approached the Rabbi, bent over his books in the study.

"My father," he said, "all is in readiness for my departure tomorrow. Most gratefully again do I thank you for all you have done, for the sacrifices you and my mother have made to permit me to study in Mainz."

"You will do well there," replied the Rabbi, affectionately, "and be a credit to us and to our holy religion. Eventually, you will be a great rabbi—much greater than I, my son."

"Never that," said Samson.

"But yes. All these many years, since you were no more than five, for this have I striven. Work hard in Mainz, avoid all sinful and pernicious influences. Never fail your God, your synagogue, or your people—and I will live to be very proud of you."

Samson felt a lump in his throat as he watched the dark eyes soften in that face with the noble, sharply etched features.

"I shall try, my father, not to disappoint you."

"You couldn't," said the Rabbi, simply.

"Father, on this my last day at home for some time, I would like to ask your permission to make an excursion with my brothers."

"Excursion? But your mother has prepared a very special meal for your last night at home."

"We would be home before dark. It's just that there's a harvest festival in Beaumont. Karl Schwarz has an errand there for his father, who is lending him the horse and cart. He said he would drive us there if you would grant permission."

"You know, Samson, I do not approve of these pagan festivals."

"We would not stay long," urged Samson, "and I would keep a close eye on the boys. I would see that they spoke to no one." Then, with a new urgency: "It would give our mother a chance for a little rest."

The Rabbi of Saverne hesitated.

"Very well," he said, "but be sure to return before dark. Naturally, you will not take little Samuel or the baby."

"Oh, no. Only David, Henoch, Felkel, and Jacob. Thank you, my father."

When the boys returned from school, there was high excitement. The occasions of a family excursion had been few and far between. Happily they piled into the cart when Karl drove up to the door. Léa, with four-year-old Samuel and the baby Esther clinging to her skirts, waved them off with a smile. It was good that the brothers should have one last happy time together. She was satisfied that she had given each a thick piece of home-baked bread and a slice of cheese to carry along, each in his own small packet. To Samson, she had entrusted an extra loaf, and a knife—"just in case anyone gets especially hungry," she had explained.

The cart rolled merrily along toward the foothills of the Vosges whose crests in the late October sun were shrouded in a soft, gray-blue haze. David, endowed with a new importance by the imminent departure of his brother which would make him the eldest at home, sat beside Karl Schwarz driving the placid old mare, Lisa. Karl was a year older than Samson and worked in the countinghouse with his father, whose business he would inherit. Samson sat in the rear with his arm about Jacob, lest he should tumble out as the cart rolled over the uneven stones of the market place and took to the rough dirt roads leading to the foothills. In between sat Henoch and Felkel. The effervescent air whipped the blood to their cheeks, and beneath the olive-tinted skin of these children of Israel, there arose a healthy red glow.

Karl and Samson called back and forth to each other, across the heads of the others, as the cart bumped along, Karl asking questions about the great event of the morrow.

"I will see you in Mainz," he promised, "for my father has much business there. I may even be sent there within the next few months."

Fifteen-year-old David turned his head to the rear.

"You may be sure," he proclaimed, "that soon, when the time comes for me to go away for study, I shall not go only to Mainz; I shall go to Paris, for the best!"

"And I, too," boasted the nine-year-old Felkel. Jacob nudged closer to Samson.

Henoch, only recently turned thirteen, asked:

"Why does anyone have to go away for *study?* Why can't one join the army and go all over the world, or something?"

Jacob looked at him, horrified. Why, every son of a rabbi should become a rabbi! It was only right!

Perhaps it was the shocked expression on his face that put Henoch into a teasing mood.

"When we get to the festival," he taunted, "Jacob is going to have to remain in the cart. He's too young to be let loose!"

"Yes," chimed in Felkel, "you will have to stay in the cart and mind the horse while we go off and see all the side shows. You won't get hungry, that way—so now you can give me your packet of bread and cheese!" He made a lunge toward Jacob.

Samson expertly stopped the predatory gesture, and soundly boxed Felkel's ears.

"Who do you think you are?" he asked. "Hans Trapp?"

Felkel shrank away, abashed. The terrible Hans Trapp was the bogeyman of all Alsatian children, Israelite and Christian alike. Once, long ago, there had been a ferocious robber baron, one Jean de Dratt, who had kept his state high up in the hills, and had preyed on the helpless country people— robbing, pillaging, killing. Tales of his crimes had been handed down, from generation to generation, until finally Jean de Dratt had become "Hans Trapp," and the surest name to strike fear when children got out of hand.

Now the road was ascending sharply, and Karl let the mare go into a walk. Once in a while they would come to a cross-roads where a rustic shrine had been erected, forming a shel-ter for the figure of the Christian God on his cross. All but Samson averted their eyes—but Jacob, now without quivering. Samson alone stared curiously at the symbol, and at the occasional bouquets of wild flowers placed at its base.

Presently they encountered other carts on their way to the

carnival—women in gala native costumes, men in holiday attire. Some of the men wore a feather stuck jauntily in their hats; others, a bright flower from the fields. Ever more pungently did the perfume of the grape surround the young people in the cart. But the vineyards along the road, now denuded of their rich purple clusters, looked trampled and somehow forlorn.

Soon they were driving into the village square of Beaumont. Everywhere there were people—people and laughter and talk. Karl drove the cart to a nearby grove, and there under some tall pines released Lisa from her shafts and left her free to munch the grass and slake her thirst at a stream which meandered down the mountainside. Everyone had clambered out. With the promise to return in half an hour, Karl had set off to seek his father's friend, one of the owners of the vineyards, to dispatch his errand. Samson stood like a major general, holding his army of four at attention.

"You will stay close to me," he said quietly, "and should anyone speak to you, it will be best not to answer."

A chill suddenly fell upon their enthusiasm. They remembered now that they would be mingling with the goyim and must be careful. The enchanting prospect of visiting a festival had driven that fact from their minds. Soberly they approached the square, with Samson in the lead, holding young Jacob by the hand. Henoch and Felkel walked behind with David who had assumed the mature air of older brother. The younger ones were torn between a desire to break loose to explore the wondrous things glimpsed, and a caution bred of long inculcation.

Here was a booth where sausages and beer were being sold, and where young men and young women sat at little outdoor tables, sipping the brew, chatting gaily and laughing. There, on a raised platform, two gypsies pirouetted in flaming colors, beating the tambourine, calling customers to come and have their fortunes read. The center of the square had been roped off for dancing, and musicians, with zither and accordion, were playing a lively tune for a dozen young couples performing a folk dance. Everywhere the crowd milled and pushed.

Suddenly from out of a corner tavern, and directly across their path, staggered a huge man they all knew—the bullying Wasterhoff, blacksmith of Saverne. Almost before they had recognized him, they heard his raucous shout:

"Sons of the Rabbi of Saverne! What are you doing here? You don't belong here! This is a *Christian* festival! Go home to your father and tell him we have no place in Christian Alsace for the sons of Jewish dogs!"

Jacob seemed to shrivel up, and clung closer to Samson.

"Come," said Samson, holding the small hand tighter, "we will go back to the grove. Pay no attention to him. He is drunk."

David said in a low voice: "We three will take the longer way back. Better, if we separate."

The sober-faced group of three melted into the throng. Alone, Samson and Jacob made their way through the crowd. The carnival spirit ran high, and no one seemed to have paid the slightest attention to the drunkard Wasterhoff. Indeed, no one seemed to have heard his words—no one except the children of the Rabbi of Saverne. In the minds of these, the phrase was repeating itself over and over: "sons of Jewish dogs, sons of Jewish dogs." Their father had been called a "Jewish dog"!

Jacob recalled how his father and his teacher had constantly borne witness to the hatred in which their people were held by the goyim. But never before had he heard that hatred expressed. It struck him with a new and terrible force. After much suffering, he had been able to overcome his fear of their sign. But now a new fear had replaced it—his fear of their thought. He wanted to get quickly away from them—to be alone with his own.

"Can we not go faster?" he asked of his brother who was striding along, his face set in grim lines.

When they had reached the quiet grove where the horse was complacently grazing, Samson said:

"Let us sit down under the trees and eat our bread. The others will be along soon, and we can start homeward."

Jacob, on the grass beside his brother, chewed thoughtfully on his portion and asked:

"What did he mean when he called our father a 'Jewish dog'?"

"Oh," said Samson carelessly, "it's a way the goyim have of expressing their hatred for us. You must get used to it, Shaekle. You will hear it often. Deep down in their hearts they know we are the Chosen People of God—and they are envious."

So that was it. Well, it must be a terrible thing to suffer—to have been passed over by God. Not to be one of His Chosen. . . .

At about that time, back in the house next to the synagogue in old Saverne, a dialogue was taking place between Léa and her husband.

"I am full of unrest about our sons," said the Rabbi, pacing back and forth with hands clasped behind him. "I should not have given permission to attend the festival. No good can come of it."

"Now, my husband, do not give yourself concern. It is good that they should have a holiday in this beautiful weather. What harm could there be? Are they not with one of their own kind, Karl, the son of the banker?"

"Karl! His father allows him too much freedom, to my thinking."

"But he is now a man, even as our Samson—and must fight his way in the world."

"I shall fear greatly for Samson when he is far from us in Mainz!"

Léa put her hand on his shoulder. "Always the time comes when the birds must leave the nest, is it not so? Did it not happen to you? And did not all turn out well?"

The Rabbi gratefully patted her hand, and returned to his study. . . .

In the grove, their lunch consumed, Jacob lay back on the grass. He was tired and glad to rest. Overhead the sky was very blue, with great soft pillows of white cloud drifting lazily across the azure counterpane. He was of the Chosen People, he reflected happily. God had made him so. He loved God very much, oh, very much! Then from out of nowhere a wind came, with scarcely an audible breath, to stir the boughs of the giant pine above him. They swayed and danced to its gentle, rhythmical measure, making graceful curtsies to him. How beautiful was the wind, and how mysterious! Involuntarily, he began to recite aloud in Hebrew:

" 'Who hath ascended up into heaven, and descended? Who hath held the wind in his hands? Who hath bound up the waters together as in a garment? Who hath raised up all the borders of the earth? What is his name, and what is the name of his son, if thou knowest?' "

"From Proverbs," observed Samson. "You have learned it well."

"Father taught it to me the other day. It's beautiful, isn't it?"

Karl had now returned from his errand and was busy hitching Lisa to the cart. Suddenly there was a sound of running feet, and they looked up to see Henoch and Felkel racing toward them, with David in hot pursuit.

"They've gotten a bit out of hand," he panted.

With that, Felkel leaped high into the air, and grasping a low-hanging bough of the pine, pulled himself up like an agile monkey. Then he scrambled higher and higher, laughing as he climbed.

"David can't catch me, David can't catch me!" he chanted mockingly. In an instant, they all heard the ominous sound of the breaking bough. Before they could move, down tumbled Felkel in a heap at their feet.

"Now, see—" began David. But Samson was bending over the whimpering form.

"My arm," moaned Felkel.

Samson got behind him and gently lifted the boy to a sitting position. "Now let's see," he said soothingly.

Obviously, there was something very wrong with Felkel's left arm. Just above the elbow there was an odd protuberance.

"Wait, Felkel. Don't move. I think I can fix it."

There was a stump nearby, where a tree had been cut down. Whipping out the knife from the extra packet his mother had pressed upon him, Samson began cutting off firm slices of the tough bark.

"Give me your kerchiefs," he commanded.

The others, silent and frightened, complied. Samson approached the sobbing Felkel. "There," he said, "it's going to be all right." Deftly he adjusted the splint and bound it. Then he lifted the lad up tenderly and, carrying him as though he were a baby, placed him in the cart. But on the silent drive homeward, little Felkel was very sick indeed.

"We will need a doctor," explained Samson to the white-faced Léa as she opened the door for them. His father emerged from the study. There was a moment's silence as he surveyed the scene, while the younger children shook with fear.

"As I expected," said the Rabbi. "The punishment of God upon those who defy His law, and mingle with the goyim!"

Silently Samson carried Felkel upstairs and laid him on his bed. David had run to summon a doctor. The Rabbi stood by the boy's bed and stroked his forehead. Léa, distracted, hurried up and down stairs, carrying towels and vessels of water. Presently David returned with the doctor. Samson met them at the door and conducted the stranger upstairs. The Rabbi, with a tone of authority, ordered the trembling Léa and all but Samson from the room. There was a very long minute as the doctor examined Felkel. He probed gently at the injured arm, murmuring to himself. Then he straightened up.

"Who," he asked sternly, "adjusted this splint?"

Samson went white. "I did, sir."

"It's perfect," announced the doctor. "I could not do better, myself. I shall not disturb it. Where, young man, did you learn how to make a splint?"

Stammering, Samson outlined the episode of the accident he had witnessed a few days before. "I just watched," he said simply.

"Hum. . . . Well, young man, you should be a doctor yourself."

He turned to the Rabbi of Saverne. "Have you thought of giving your son medical training?"

The Rabbi frowned, spreading his hands in a gesture of annoyance.

"How now, should I be giving him medical training when he has spent all his life preparing to be a rabbi?" he demanded. "Even tomorrow, he leaves for Mainz to complete his rabbinical studies." Then, throwing up the fine old head: "Some day he will be a very great rabbi," he added defiantly. "It's nonsense, to put medicine into my son's head!"

Samson said nothing, but in his heart there was a strange, happy thrill. It did not leave him all that night, when he slept only fitfully. Even the next day, when he was about to mount the stagecoach and had turned once more to embrace his tearful mother and the tight-lipped rabbi, it was still with him.

Only Jacob had been permitted to come with his parents to see Samson off. Now he flung himself into his brother's arms.

"Become a great rabbi," he whispered, "a very great rabbi. For then no one will ever again dare call our father a Jewish dog!"

CHAPTER THREE

The Loss

It was march of 1811 and the Passover was approaching. The full moon of Nisan, when the great feast would be observed, was at hand.

Three years had passed since Samson had left for Mainz, and his brief visits home had not been frequent. Mainz had matured him, and at the same time added a greater reserve. His attitude toward his father had somehow undergone a subtle change. Though seeming to enjoy the animated discussions on abstract points of the Law, in which his scholarship delighted the Rabbi, he yet seemed anxious to terminate them quickly. To his father's periodic and ever solicitous question, "Do you need money, my son?" Samson's reply was always the same: "You are most generous, my father. What you are sending amply suffices."

His relationship to his mother had not changed, and held all its old youthful tenderness. Nevertheless, to her sorrow, Samson had sent word that he could not be with them this Passover.

David, at eighteen, now had assumed the primacy of the oldest brother, and soon his time, too, would come for study abroad. Constantly he urged his father to send him to Paris where famous rabbinical schools had long been established.

Jacob, who would soon be nine, had found an ever-widening beauty and meaning in the Passover. For days now he had watched his mother purifying the house as prescribed by the precepts of Passah. He had seen her carefully take down the dishes which were used only once a year, had listened as she explained the important separation of the "pure" from the "impure."

When at length the eve of the holy days had arrived, he had looked on with interest as the paschal food was being prepared: horse-radish, for the bitterness of Egyptian slavery; applesauce, for the clay of Egypt; the lamb, whose blood had marked the doorposts of the Israelites—a signal to the Lord's angel to pass over them when smiting the first-born of the Egyptians—and which now had been both killed and cooked according to strict religious formula; and finally the unleavened bread, the only food that could be taken during the seven solemn days following upon the eve, and commemorating the Exodus.

Because David was the oldest son at home, it was he who recited the *Haggada* on the eve of the Passover. And as youngest, it fell to little Esther, who was seated next to Jacob, to put the age-old question: *"Mah nishtanah haleilah haseh micol haleiloth?*—What is the difference between this night and all other nights?" The question, from his earliest memory, had never failed to enthrall Jacob. But this night it struck him with a new solemnity.

The ritual of the *Haggada* called for the drinking of wine

at intervals, in which the entire family, from oldest to youngest, joined. With the others Jacob reverently dipped his fingers
ten times into the wine, to signify the ten plagues of Egypt. It
was a delicious paschal meal which Léa had prepared, but Jacob was so intent upon all it signified that he was conscious of
little else, except of a hidden, dull pang he felt throughout—
that on this night, Samson was missing. Never before had
Samson failed to observe the Passover at home with his own.
What could have happened? He had written that his studies
would keep him in Mainz; but Jacob knew that had not satisfied his father. He had watched the Rabbi as Léa had read
the letter aloud and had seen the shadow that fell upon the
beloved face. Lazarus Libermann had sat silent for a few
moments, then with slow steps and bent head had sought out
his study and closed the door. From that moment, Jacob determined to observe these holy days more carefully, more
rigidly, than ever; to try as never before to please his father;
above all, in his daily and secret prayers to implore the Almighty to bless his brother Samson.

When the seven days had been accomplished, the Rabbi
called Jacob to his study.

"Your behavior during the holy time has pleased me
greatly," he said. "You are growing up, my Shaekle, and from
now on I shall not address you by your baby name. From now
on, you will be Jacob, my beloved son. Continue to study well
and observe all things; continue to love God above all, toward
the end that some day you will gladden your father's heart
by following in his path."

"I will try very hard, my father."

"Good. And now, I would ask you to do me a service."

"Gladly."

The Rabbi's long sensitive fingers sought among the parchments on his desk. He held up a much-worn, ink-stained quill.

"I need some new pens," he explained, "but the difficulty is that friend Klotz, from whom I usually obtain them, is ill at home and his shop is closed for the time. It leaves no other choice than to buy from the goyim."

"If you need them for your work—" began Jacob.

"That's just it. The work cannot wait. I must have them today. So you will go to the shop of the widow Schaeffer, there on the market place. Do not tarry or speak more than is necessary. Make your purchase quietly—six new quills, no longer than this—and quickly return."

"Yes, my father."

"Here is a five franc note. There will be change. Count it before you leave the shop, lest there be an error; and guard it carefully. The quills should not cost more than one franc. So it is four francs that you should return to me."

Jacob nodded and smiled happily. For more reasons than one he was delighted with this errand. Walking along briskly, he paused now and then to make sure that the precious note was still safe in the inner pocket of his jacket.

The shop of the widow Schaeffer was on the ground floor of an ancient building facing the market place. Above it extended one of those overhanging stories which Jacob, when younger, had fancied might tumble down upon him. What a baby he had been in those days, he reflected as he approached it. Afraid of old buildings, of grotesque stone faces—of the symbol of the goyim. Being almost nine gave one a feeling of great superiority.

He had long been attracted by this particular shop, although he had never entered it. But many times had he paused before its window, set with small square panes of glass heavily leaded together. They displayed objects which held for him an uncontrollable fascination. They were books. Books large and small, bound in soft leather, fawn-colored and brown, with their titles in gold lettering. Many a time had he lingered to spell out the letters to himself, and wistfully to wonder what lay within their covers. Now he would have a chance to see them at closer range.

A little bell tinkled as he timidly opened the door, and a stout lady behind a counter looked up from the volume she was displaying to a tall, white-haired gentleman. Signaling Jacob to enter, she again bent over the tome and continued her conversation with the customer, leaving the boy free to wander about and gaze at the shelves which lined the walls. They were crowded with books and pamphlets, and he longed to handle them but dared not. He thought there was nothing quite as beautiful as fine, leather-bound books placed against ancient, dark gleaming oak. Here were no titles that he had ever seen in his father's study, or indeed anywhere— and he was filled with a vast curiosity.

Presently the widow completed her transaction and abruptly motioned him to approach. "She looks cross," thought Jacob. When he had shyly stated his errand, she opened a drawer beneath the counter and drew forth a tray of quill pens, the ends of which had been well cut into shapely points. Timidly indicating the size he desired, Jacob drew out the five franc note and asked what the price would be for six.

"One franc," said the widow crisply, laying out the pens and seizing the note.

As she turned to her cashbox to make change, again the

bell tinkled and with it also the laughter and talk of women. They were two: young, beautiful, and dressed in the latest fashion. Jacob had never seen anyone like them before, and gazed in wonderment. Their bonnets alone were fabulous, feathered things. The widow, who had looked up from her money as they entered, was obviously delighted, and her sour demeanor underwent a sudden and radical change.

"*Madame la Comtesse!*" she cried joyously, her face wreathed in smiles. "Ah, you have come back for the wonderful Shakespeare."

Hastily thrusting some coins at Jacob, she hurried forward to greet the two ladies.

"I can resist it no longer," confessed the countess gaily, "although you know as well as I, that the price is too high. Why, in Paris—"

"Ah, no," protested the widow. "You see, Madame, it is. . . ."

Jacob reluctantly withdrew his eyes and reached for the change upon the counter. And there, to his surprise, instead of four francs, he saw five. He hesitated. It was obvious that the widow, in the flurry of excitement over her exalted customers, had overpaid him by one franc. He looked over at the buzzing little group. It would take courage to interrupt her now. Then suddenly a thought struck him. Had not the schoolmaster repeatedly said that it was virtue to cheat the goyim? Why, this would please his father. And quickly pocketing the quills and the money, he made for the door. The three women, bent over a large and beautifully bound folio, did not even look up as the door closed.

He was so stimulated that he ran much of the way home. The study door was open, and entering breathlessly, he smil-

ingly placed the new quills upon the desk. Then taking the
money from his pocket, he counted it out dramatically, franc
by franc, under his father's nose.

"One, two, three, four, five. And they cost one franc!" he
said triumphantly.

"But here are five francs. All you had."

"I know. And it is to win merit before the Almighty that I
return with the extra franc. The schoolmaster said—" He
paused for breath, and then rushed on: "The widow Schaeffer
did not notice—and I thought you would be pleased!"

The Rabbi looked at him a moment uncomprehendingly,
then leaned back in his chair and gave vent to one of his rare
chuckles.

"Ah, I understand," he said, his eyes gleaming with mirth.
"A transaction with the goyim! You were indeed alert, my
son." And then suddenly serious again, he leaned forward and
took Jacob's two hands in his.

"This interpretation is sometimes accepted. But there are
some things about it, my son. . . . Let us talk it all out at
length some other day. Meantime, I think it's better that you
observe strict honesty in *all* your dealings—no matter with
whom."

"Yes, Father," said Jacob, considerably crestfallen.

That night as he was preparing for bed and laying out his
books for school the next morning, Jacob reflected upon the
day's adventure. So the schoolmaster had not been right,
after all. Unlike his father, he did not know everything. If
Mendelbaum had been wrong about this—and everything
within Jacob's spirit told him he had been wrong—it could
well be that he was not infallible about other things. Suddenly Jacob realized that he no longer feared the schoolmas-

ter. He straightened up from the neat pile he had been arranging on the chair, and drew a long breath, flinging out his arms.

"What is it, brother Jacob?" asked seven-year-old Samuel, already in bed, his bright dark eyes peering from under the white coverlet.

"Only that I feel suddenly very well, Samuel, and that I would like to sing."

"Well, don't," said Samuel, again burying his head. "I'm sleepy."

But when Jacob had finished his last prayers and the candle had been extinguished, he lay awake for a long time enjoying this new attitude toward the schoolmaster. With his advancing years and experience, yet another fear which had formerly chilled him had melted away. First, the overhanging buildings, the hideous stone faces, the sign of the goyim—and now, the schoolmaster. Why, life was wonderful, and not to be feared at all. He felt very contented and secure as he dropped off to sleep.

Only three of the brothers started for school together the next morning—Felkel, who was now twelve, and Jacob and Samuel. Henoch, sixteen, had advanced to the higher school. He and David had been on their way somewhat earlier. For the three younger boys the first school hours passed creditably, and Jacob had even wrung a "Very good!" from the schoolmaster's thin lips upon his recitation of a lesson in geography. But when the time allotted for secular studies had passed, Mendelbaum launched out upon his favorite topic— the danger of mingling with the goyim. He related the story of a pious Jew who had once gazed too long upon a cross.

"God cursed him," declared the teacher with great emphasis. "He lost all his property, he was stricken blind, his wife and children died painful deaths, and he ended his life as a beggar."

The schoolmaster paused dramatically. Then pitching his voice on a higher key, "This should teach you," he cried, "to fear that sign as you fear nothing else."

There was a moment's heavy stillness in that schoolroom of some twenty Jewish boys. Then was the air electrified by a clear young voice from the fourth row:

"I do not fear it."

Everyone was startled; everyone stared at Jacob. The schoolmaster, his prominent near-sighted eyes opening wider behind the square spectacles, gazed open-mouthed at the offender.

"What did you say, Jacob Libermann? Repeat that!"

"I do not fear the sign of the goyim," repeated the boy firmly.

A dark red overspread Mendelbaum's countenance, starting at his neck and working upward.

"You do not fear their sign? And how now, did you come to discover this, my friend?" The schoolmaster's tone was as cold and sharp as a steel knife. And before he had realized how awful was the confession, Jacob had blurted out:

"Once I entered their synagogue—"

He got no further. In an instant, and before he could explain, Mendelbaum was out of his chair and had fallen upon him. Felkel and Samuel hid their faces in their hands. They knew what was coming. In a flash Jacob knew also, but felt curiously calm. Let it come, then. Others before him, had received it. So then, could he.

Now Mendelbaum had him by the ankles and was swing-

ing his head against the wall—once, twice, thrice. Other lads
of nine had been heavier, thought the schoolmaster contemp-
tuously, as he flung Jacob back onto the bench and dusted
his hands with a large kerchief. Why, this young weakling
did not weigh more than a boy of seven.

Felkel in the last row, with blanched knuckles, was still
gripping the edge of the bench. Young Samuel in the second
row was openly sobbing. But Jacob's body only trembled
slightly as he mopped the cut on his brow from which the
blood was freely flowing. Not a tear did he shed—but his
young teeth were tightly clenched and his jaw set. Boys older
than he, victims who had wept freely on similar occasions,
stared at him in amazement.

"Go home," said the schoolmaster harshly, "and show the
Rabbi of Saverne how Mendelbaum punishes those who are
guilty of blasphemy. Tell him, you, that his son does not fear
the sign of the goyim. Tell him that the son of the Rabbi is so
brave that he has even entered into their church!" His voice
had risen to a shrill scream. "This should *please* the Rabbi of
Saverne!" . . .

How his head ached and throbbed. It was dark in the room,
for Léa had blown out the candle. Samuel was already asleep.
The house was very still. He reached up and gingerly touched
the bandage his mother had adjusted. Then he reached out
for her hand where she sat there, close by his bed in the
dark.

"Mother mine," he whispered.

"Yes, my Shaekle," Léa bent over him. The baby name had
escaped her in spite of herself. "Shall I bring you more cool
water?"

"Please."

He drank avidly from the cup she held. Gently she felt his cheeks and his hands. They were very hot. . . . ("O beloved and Almighty Father, give him strength to overcome the cruel blows.")

"Try now to sleep, Shaekle."

"Yes, Mother."

He lay back on the pillow with a sigh. How good his parents had been to him! His mother had wept at the sight of him, had bathed and bandaged his head, and put him to bed. But his father—he could not get over his father. It was wonderful! As the story had poured out in broken sentences from his swollen lips, the Rabbi had listened gravely. When Jacob had come to the part about the church, his father had sharply interrupted:

"But this was not blasphemy! You did not know wherein you were entering. You entered not willfully, but ignorantly. The Law condones such."

Jacob felt greatly comforted—as though a heavy load had been lifted from his breast.

"Did you not explain to Mendelbaum?"

"He would not listen," said Jacob.

"But you are wrong not to fear the sign of the goyim," continued his father. "It could do you great harm. It is because you are young and innocent that you think otherwise. You will learn. But now hearken, as to school: You are not to return—at least for some weeks. You will continue your studies with me for a time. How will you like that, eh?"

A great joy had filled him, and he had tried to smile, but it hurt the sore on his cheek.

"Oh, thank you, my father."

"And I shall see Mendelbaum tomorrow and explain all.

No one must think that a son of mine entered a church of the goyim willfully!"

So Jacob would not have to see the schoolmaster again for a while. How good! . . . and finally he had drifted off to sleep. But the next morning Léa found she had a very sick boy on her hands. . . .

On a day not long after this, and when his ninth birthday had come and gone, he was working on a passage from the Torah under his father's eye. The cut on his forehead had almost healed, and save for the bad headaches which came now and then—and of which he said nothing—he was well again. But his father had not mentioned a return to school, and kept Jacob busy much of the time in his study. It was warm, on this particular day, and because the study which faced the street received the full glare of the morning sun, the curtain had been drawn almost across the window, leaving only a narrow slit permitting light to fall upon the Rabbi's desk.

That was why they could not see who it was whose footsteps they had heard coming up the street—footsteps which had at first slowed, and then stopped altogether before the front door. They listened for a knock, but it did not come. It was as though someone were hesitating there.

Jacob lifted his head. Suddenly his mind was torn from the Torah to make way compellingly for the vivid picture of his brother Samson—Samson who was far away in Mainz. The knock never came, but presently they heard the street door open. In another moment Samson stood before them.

The Rabbi, stupefied for an instant, rose joyously to embrace his oldest son, while Jacob danced happily around his brother as their father poured forth a torrent of welcome in Hebrew. Samson, grinning happily, put an arm about each.

"Your mother!" cried the Rabbi. "She will be overjoyed. Come, let us find her."

From Samson's sensitive lips the smile faded.

"A moment first, Father. I would speak to you first alone." He gave his young brother a meaning glance.

Jacob, who had been gazing in admiration at this tall, splendid young man, said at once:

"I will run over to the *quai*. When you want me to fetch Mother, you can call to me from the window."

In a moment he was in the street. Leaning on the railing and looking down upon the *quai*, he scarcely saw what was going on there. To be sure, some housewives were stooping over the canal and washing clothes; others were rinsing them in tubs of water, and wringing them dry. Their jolly, gossipy chatter rose shrilly on the morning air. But Jacob did not hear.

Something must be wrong with Samson—very wrong. Why had he not told them he was coming? The holy days were long since over. It would be a good six days before the next Sabbath. This was not a time for holiday. Why had Samson hesitated at the door before entering? It was his own door, his own home, his own family. Why, above all, had he insisted upon talking with their father first, before he had even greeted their mother?

Jacob tried to still the apprehension which was choking him, causing his breath to come sharply. Would they never call to him? It seemed to him that he had been there an hour. First one elbow and then the next had grown so sore from leaning on the iron railing that now he let both arms fall and sat down dejectedly, letting his legs dangle over the stone abutment. Time dragged. When he thought he could endure it no longer and would have to invent some excuse for returning to the house, he heard Samson's voice calling him.

In an instant he was on his feet, and had burst into the study almost before Samson had turned from the window. When he saw their faces, he knew at once that something momentous had occurred. For the Rabbi's face was dark with anger, and he had never seen Samson look so white and ill at ease.

"Shall I call our mother?" he managed to stammer.

"No," said Samson shortly. "I shall go and find her myself."

As he left, he closed the door behind him. Now the Rabbi collapsed into his chair and, with elbows on the desk, buried his face in his hands. Jacob, with sinking heart, approached him timidly.

"What is it, Father?" His voice was no more than a whisper.

Lazarus Libermann looked up, then put his arm about the young figure. He made no attempt to hide his tears as he said brokenly:

"Your brother has abandoned his studies. He will not go on. He will never give glory to our holy religion, or help his people, as it was planned. He will never be a rabbi."

Jacob could only gasp his astonishment. With difficulty, his father continued:

"He in whom I had placed my greatest hope! My first-born— After all the long years of preparation—I trained him myself—then, not trusting myself fully, I made sacrifices to send him where he would get the best. And all this time, I have supported him. Ah, but he has not been faithful, your brother Samson. He must have had this—this lunacy—in his mind for a long time!"

"If not a rabbi, what then will he be?" asked the mystified Jacob.

"He declares he will study medicine. Medicine, of all things! He would become a doctor! He asks my help. But I will not give it him! I will not give it him!" The tears had ceased, and the Rabbi's voice was harsh. "He has chosen his own way. Well then, let him find his own way." The eagle-head went up in a gesture of angry defiance.

Jacob put his arms about his father's neck. His heart ached with sympathy for him, and for Samson—but his tongue could find no words. This was indeed the worst calamity that had yet befallen the family. Samson not to be a rabbi! His mind kept dully repeating the words, then rejecting them, only to repeat them again. For a long time they remained thus. Then the Rabbi drew Jacob close to him.

"You are now our great hope, my Jacob. From the start it was you and Samson who possessed all the qualities. I doubt much about the others—although they too must try, must be trained. But you, of you I am sure, and have been for long. So now you must work harder than ever. And you will never disappoint your father, will you, my Jacob?"

"Never, Father." The boy's voice rang out, clear and determined. . . .

What passed that morning between Samson and his mother, only they two ever knew. But after Samson had sadly departed that same day, Léa wept continuously and seemed inconsolable. For days the Rabbi scarcely spoke—and none dared approach him. Indeed, he spent the greater part of every day at prayer in the synagogue. Once, at supper, Léa had timidly asked him:

"Could we not, Lazarus, help our Samson a little with money, in his new work? It will be hard—"

"No!" exclaimed the Rabbi. "He has chosen. So be it."

On that memorable morning Jacob had been alone with his brother for five brief minutes. He had clung to Samson's hand and gazed up into the sternly set features. Again, he could say nothing. But Samson, his arm about the boy's shoulders, had said:

"Do not grieve. You and I will never part, really. Soon you will be grown, and sent away for study yourself. Then we shall meet again. I will contrive, somehow, that we may be near. Meantime, work hard, for you, not I, must become the great Rabbi Libermann! And Jacob—"

"Yes, Samson?"

"Ever be kind and docile with Father. He is good—"

Samson's voice had broken a little, and he had looked away. . . .

In the months that followed a pall settled permanently over the house. The Rabbi had visibly aged and shut himself even more away from his family. Almost immediately after Samson's visit he had sent Jacob back to school. The boy had returned without any resentment in his heart against the schoolmaster, who seemed indeed to have lost much of his fiery choler since the episode involving the Rabbi's son. Jacob, to his surprise and actual embarrassment, found himself something of a hero in the eyes of his schoolmates. They treated him with a new respect and affection.

Léa's step was heavier as she moved about the house; she said little, and sighed frequently. To her it seemed that Jacob had grown up over night. He applied himself with even greater diligence to his studies; frequently he slipped into the synagogue for a quiet hour of prayer. And he ignored the erstwhile fascinations of the once absorbing *quai.*

On the other hand, David, Henoch, and Felkel seemed to remain almost unaffected by the events of that spring morning. In fact, rather than being saddened, they found a secret excitement and pride in the prospect of their oldest brother becoming a doctor. Among themselves they could speak of it and conjecture about it, as they did frequently—but never before their parents or Jacob. And now, somewhat derisively, yet also affectionately, behind his back Henoch and Felkel began to refer to Jacob as "the little Rabbi." The small ones, Samuel and Esther, busy at their play, were too young to understand the import of what had happened.

When, some months later, David's eighteenth birthday approached, he went hopefully to his father.

"Now that I am almost eighteen, my father, how soon will you arrange to send me to Paris to complete my studies?"

"Not for two years more," snapped the Rabbi. "Samson went away at eighteen. It was too young, as we have learned to our sorrow. No more of my sons will be permitted to leave home until they have reached the age of twenty. By then it is to be hoped they will be mature enough to remain steadfast, and not be shaken by the idle tongues and foolish fancies of the goyim."

And David, glum-faced and restless, had to content himself with the prospect of two more long years in Saverne, of which he was heartily sick.

During those two years, Samson never came again, but frequently Léa received long letters from him, which at the

Rabbi's expressed request she never showed him or spoke about. Only once in a while would she take Jacob aside and read him what his brother had written. Samson had found employment as a teacher. He was living in utmost poverty, using the greater part of his earnings to pay for medical studies. Léa and Jacob prayed constantly for him.

Jacob's father spoke to him more frequently now about his future as a rabbi, and everything at home and in school was made to pivot about that goal. And Jacob was content—except at those times when the loss of Samson would overcome him, and he would seek a secluded spot and give himself over to his silent grief, grief for his sorely disappointed father, grief for his sorrowing mother, grief for Samson that he had foresworn so noble a career, and grief for himself that he had lost the presence and the counsel of that warm heart and steadying hand.

On such occasions the headaches which had become familiars ever since the schoolmaster had flung him against the wall would recur with blinding intensity. But he never spoke of them.

Finally, when two years had passed, David was permitted, with many severe admonitions and following the Rabbi's careful correspondence with friends in the rabbinical schools of Paris, to leave for that city. Now it was Henoch's turn to move into the place of the oldest son at home.

Her brood was diminishing, thought Léa sadly, as she looked at the young faces gathered about the supper table. Only Henoch, Felkel, Jacob, and Samuel left—and little Esther. One by one they would all be taken from her. It was only a matter of a few years. But she would make the best of those years. She would continue to feed them well, and watch over their health, and make them as happy as she could.

With red and gold fingers of fire, the autumn of 1813 had now touched the slopes of the Vosges. The grapes had been gathered in, the wine casks were full; and for the past week a cold rain had been falling steadily from sodden skies upon the streets of Saverne. Léa, preparing supper in the kitchen, pulled a shawl closer about her shoulders. No matter how high she tried to keep the fire, she had been shivering this past hour. That morning she had made a visit to a young woman who was soon to bear her first child. They were newcomers to the Rabbi's congregation, this young couple, arrived recently from Germany, and had been forced to take temporary lodgings on the other side of the market place.

Léa had walked both ways in the pouring rain, and during the course of her visit had busied herself actively, making coffee and straightening up the place while she forced the young wife to rest. Now, bending over her own fire, she was impatient with her trembling hands. The boys would be hungry when they came in. Henoch was busy with the Rabbi in his study, copying down records; but Felkel was out visiting a friend, and eleven-year-old Jacob had gone on an errand for his father and had taken Samuel with him.

Esther, now a dark-eyed, soft-voiced little girl of seven, was helping her mother in the kitchen. Léa uncertainly laid down the spoon she had been wielding over a generous kettle of soup.

"I can do no more," she said weakly to the child. "Perhaps, if I should go and rest for a space—" She dropped into a chair, gasping.

Esther, alarmed at the flushed face and trembling limbs,

quickly ran for her father. At the sight of Léa huddled in the chair, the Rabbi tried to conceal his uneasiness with a show of severity.

"What is all this? Your mother ill, and you did not call me sooner?"

"I—I had not noticed, Father."

"You will follow us and help her to bed." Gently lifting his wife from the chair, he supported her with his arm and led her up the stairs. Like a child, Léa clung to him, and the heat of her hands burned through his sleeve. When he came down he dispatched Henoch at once for a doctor. . . .

An hour later, their errand completed, Jacob and Samuel rounded the corner of the familiar street and approached the house. Jacob heaved an involuntary sigh.

"What is it, Jacob?"

"I don't know. It's—it's—well, it's quite suddenly that I feel a strange weight upon my heart."

"Why, a moment ago you were laughing!"

Henoch met them at the door, a finger to his lips.

"Mother," he whispered, and pointed upstairs. But as Jacob made to run past him, he held him by the arm.

"Father is with her now. The doctor has just left."

It was a silent and sorry supper to which, some time later, the anxious little group sat down. The Rabbi and Jacob could touch nothing—and could not have done so, had it been the best meal in the world. They spoke in whispers.

"What did the doctor say, Father?"

"That your mother has contracted an inflammation upon her lungs. That she is very sick; the fever, very severe. He has left remedies, and will be here again in the morning. One or two of us will sit by her side all night." Then, brushing his eyes with his hand, "She should not have gone out in the rain this morning. An errand of mercy. I tried to stop her, but without success. It has always been so. It would have been easier to stop Noah from entering the ark, than it is to stop your mother when bent upon an errand of mercy."

It was Jacob who did the major share of that anxious watch by night. Once when he was alone with his mother and was adjusting the coverlet which in her restlessness she kept tossing off, she feebly took his hand.

"Shaekle?"

"Yes, my mother."

"You will always stay close to God—won't you?"

"Oh yes! I promise." Then, laying a compress on her brow: "You will soon be well again, dear mother."

"We don't know," she whispered weakly. "May the will of the Eternal One be done." And she turned her face to the wall. . . .

Just three days later, death knocked at the door of the Rabbi of Saverne—and would not be gainsaid.

All of Jewish Saverne pitied them, and grieved. For Léa had been much loved. The Rabbi, inconsolable in his grief, gathered his children together about the still form, just before the funeral.

"O Lord," he prayed, "Who art full of compassion, Who dwellest on high—God of forgiveness, Who art merciful, slow to anger and abounding in lovingkindness, grant pardon of transgressions, nearness of salvation, and perfect rest beneath the shadow of Thy divine presence, in the exalted places among the holy and pure, who shine as the brightness of the firmament, to Léa, who hath gone to her eternal home.

"We beseech Thee, O Lord of compassion, remember unto

her for good all the meritorious and pious deeds which she wrought while on earth. Open unto her the gates of righteousness and light, the gates of pity and grace. O shelter her forevermore under the cover of Thy wings; and let her soul be bound up in the bond of eternal life. The Lord is her inheritance; may she rest in peace. . . ."

But later, during the funeral in the synagogue which was thronged, a different prayer silently went up.

"O Eternal Father," prayed Jacob, "was *this* Your will? Oh, why could You not have left her with us?" Sobs stifled him; he hung his head to hide the burning tears. . . .

In the small house next to the synagogue, the days which followed dragged by, heavy with intolerable grief. A cousin of Léa's, a spinster, had come to supervise the house for a time until the Rabbi could find a housekeeper. Jacob, much alone in the synagogue, praying constantly, seeking perpetual solitude, was conscious of a query gnawing interminably at his heart. Finally he could bear it no longer and sought out his father.

Lazarus Libermann, strangely transformed into an old man, sat with head bowed over his desk, quill and parchment oddly at rest.

"Father?"

The fine face marked with sorrow looked up.

"Yes, Jacob?"

"What have the Prophets said about death?"

"Why—that it's death."

"But surely, for His Chosen People—?"

"The Messiah will free us from death."

"So then—we must wait?"

"Patiently, my son, loving and fearing God."

CHAPTER FOUR

The Torah

THUS, AT ELEVEN, Jacob had learned bereavement and had looked upon the face of death. As though the defection of Samson and the severance of this beloved brother from the family circle had not been sufficient chastisement, the Almighty had seen fit to extinguish in the house of Libermann the light around which that orbit had spun. Now deprived of its control, it rocked hither and thither like a crazy thing, without order, without system—above all, without joy.

Each morning Jacob greeted the dawn with a leaden heart. It was painful to awaken only to grief. Of what account, the day ahead? Whatever adventures might befall, his dearest confidante was missing, her whose arms had ever given him shelter and understanding. And the grief-stricken father, in the past a companion in his studies and always one to rejoice in his progress, now looked upon the school reports with dulled eyes and listened with unheeding ears.

It took Jacob many months to learn to stifle that impulse

he had known as long as he could remember—to share all his experiences with his mother. Whenever the slightest thing out of the ordinary had happened, he had run to tell her all about it. The impulse now was stronger than his sense of actuality; for several times a day his muscles would tighten in the preparatory act of taking off—only to relax again despondently as the realization returned that no longer was there someone to whom he could run.

His father had said that with the coming of the Messiah all death and mourning would end. If the Messiah would only come—now! How much Jacob needed him—now! His elders had said that it might be any day . . . but then, before his elders, how many other generations of elders had said the same thing? Yet had they died without seeing him. Their graves must number into the millions, Jacob reflected. For aeons they had been dying in every quarter of the globe; and still the Messiah had not come. Could he then dare to hope, insignificant as he was, to see the Messiah in his own time, when so many great and holy ones had been denied? Why had the Almighty deferred so long in fulfilling His promise of salvation to His Chosen People? It was said, because Israel had angered Him by not keeping His Law.

Jacob's father had counseled patience. Ah, how patient those long generations of Jews had been! Jacob now began to understand why he loved the faces of the old people. It was because they had learned patience; and what they had learned was stamped with benignity upon their faces.

When such thoughts came Jacob knew that he must hasten to perfect himself within the spirit—and in his studies. Thus only would he be ready in all ways, when the time should come, to lead his people in observing the Law and in pleasing the Almighty and so to hasten the advent of the Messiah. For all hearts yearned, even as did his. And while at the age of eleven he felt weak and powerless, within his soul he had a conviction that upon his confirmation as a Jew, upon the great *Bar Mitzvah,* now only two years hence, he would be endowed with a mystical strength and wisdom to fit him as nothing else could for his predetermined role in life. . . .

The sad winter having passed, and spring now advancing, he frequently took solitary tramps into the countryside. Flinging himself down on his back to gaze up at the sky through the trees as he had done on that long ago day at the harvest festival, he would wait for the wind. Presently it would come, at first as though on tiptoe and with a whisper; and then louder and louder until with a rushing it had set the green branches to bowing in obeisance, swaying to its will, and the myriad leaves to dancing and clapping in rhythmical ritual. At such times it almost seemed to him that the long-awaited One was in the wind. So now he began to search the Prophets more diligently for all things that had been promised regarding the Saviour; and carefully to memorize the passages in Hebrew.

"Therefore the Lord himself shall give you a sign. Behold, a virgin shall conceive, and bear a son, and his name shall be called Emmanuel." "And there shall come forth a rod out of the root of Jesse, and a flower shall rise up out of his root. And the spirit of the Lord shall rest upon him, the spirit of wisdom and of understanding, the spirit of counsel and of fortitude, the spirit of knowledge and of godliness. . . . But he shall judge the poor with justice and shall reprove with equity for the meek of the earth. . . .

"The wolf shall dwell with the lamb, and the leopard shall

lie down with the kid; the calf and the lion and the sheep
shall abide together; and a little child shall lead them. . . .

"In that day, the root of Jesse, who standeth for an ensign
of the people; him the Gentiles shall beseech, and his sep-
ulchre shall be glorious."

". . . and all flesh shall know that I am the Lord that save
thee, and thy Redeemer the Mighty One of Jacob."

The cousin of his mother, Sarah Stein, a quiet spinster of
thirty who had come to help the desolate family upon Léa's
death, had offered to stay on; and the Rabbi, after several
unsuccessful attempts to find a housekeeper, had gratefully
acquiesced. Unobtrusive and shy, Sarah tried to keep the
household running. At first, in spite of all her good will, she
had been awkward, and not being as experienced as Léa had
been in matters of the home, nor a competent cook, she had
made many errors. But through all, her good will had shone,
and gradually she had improved and had learned the ways,
the tastes, and the temperaments of the family. There were
six she must care for: the Rabbi and the older boys, Henoch,
Felkel, and Jacob; and the two younger children, Samuel and
Esther.

Jacob had pitied her in her first embarrassed and unsuccessful efforts. She was doing her best for their helpless, grief-
dazed father, and so Jacob determined to do his best for her.
This obviously meant taking the younger ones off her hands
as much as possible, so when school hours were over he made
nine-year-old Samuel his companion, trying to reproduce for
him some of the comradeship which Samson had once bestowed so generously upon him. As for Esther, she was included as much as possible in their walks and pastimes.

Henoch, seventeen, and Felkel, fourteen, went their own way and were no burden to Sarah.

When a year had passed in this manner, one day the Rabbi called his five children into the study. They hoped it was not for a reprimand—such a summons was not infrequent—but their father's face reassured them. For the first time since Léa's death, a little smile played about the corners of the stern mouth.

"I have called you here to tell you that you are very fortunate. You are to have a new mother."

In the astonished silence which ensued, passing footsteps outside on the street sounded like those of giants. Jacob's heart fluttered wildly—and then seemed to die within him. A new mother! He could not comprehend.

"It is our good Sarah," continued the Rabbi, "she who has taken care of us during the long, sad months of mourning—she who is cousin to your own beloved mother."

He took Esther's small hand in his and put an arm about Samuel. "Will it not be good," he asked, "again to have a mother?"

They nodded and smiled. But the faces of Jacob and the two older boys registered something beyond shock. The Rabbi turned to them:

"It will at first seem hard to you, I think, to consider that anyone, however kind and good, is to be put in the place of your own mother. Surely children never lived more blessed by the Almighty in the virtuous mother He was pleased to give. But 'the Lord gave, and the Lord hath taken away; blessed be the name of the Lord!' His holy will be done! And now I think your hearts should find rejoicing that He has given us another who loves us and who will try to be a true mother to all. Rejoice then, if not for yourselves, then for the two little ones who when so young were bereft—for the little sister who otherwise would grow up lonely in a house of men —and rejoice for your father, that a companion has been sent to fill the lonely hours he has known since the great sorrow came upon this house."

Jacob was the first to fling his arms about his father's neck. "I am glad, my father."

Then Henoch and Felkel, too, embraced the Rabbi; and when later the five trooped out into the kitchen to tell Sarah she was welcome, there were happy smiles upon the faces of all. . . .

Twelve months before, David, far away in Paris, had grieved sorely upon the news of his mother's death, but it had occurred so soon after his departure from home that the Rabbi had not encouraged a hasty journey back to Saverne at that time. Now, however, since the reports of his progress throughout the year had been favorable, Lazarus, writing his son of the forthcoming marriage, invited him home for the event. But to Samson he sent no word. True, upon Léa's sudden demise, he had instructed Henoch to notify his brother in Strasbourg; but Samson, overwhelmed with grief and only barely able to subsist on his meager earnings, could not have afforded the journey home, even had there been no estrangement between him and his father.

David followed his younger brothers in welcoming Sarah into the family; and all Jewish Saverne was pleased at the fitness of the match. However, when the flurry was over and David had departed again for Paris to resume his studies, there were left three at home who carried a burden upon their hearts. The two youngest, to whom Sarah was really attached, quickly turned to her. For them she had indeed become a second mother. But for the three older boys there could be no real substitute for her to whom from earliest memory they had confided all their problems, struggles, and ambitions. Their history with her had been too long; their memories covered such a span of constant sympathy, in joy or in trouble, and they had known such a tender intimacy with her that they shrank from endowing Sarah with anything like a similar status. How, they asked themselves, could this comparative stranger, whom formerly they had known only as a guest perhaps twice a year at the great family feasts, ever understand them?

All of this, out of loyalty to their father, each kept strictly to himself. But each in his way reacted differently to the new situation. A restlessness possessed Henoch which was obvious to the entire household. As a lad he had fancied himself a soldier; and in later years had more than once shown a resistance to the rabbinical training. Now at eighteen he was well aware that the French armies encouraged the enlistment even of youths of seventeen. When in the preceding year, 1813, he had learned of the English invasion of France, of the powerful coalition against her, with Prussia, Russia, Sweden, England, and Austria all bent upon the overthrow of the Emperor Napoleon, he had chafed to go with the latter's forces which had won the victories at Dresden, at Lützen, and at Bautzen. But he knew that his father would not only oppose it but would also make him a victim of his anger and scorn. Therefore he had not dared reveal the longing.

But now that another woman had replaced his mother, now that things at home would never be the same again, he summoned the courage to speak. At first the Rabbi had re-

ceived the idea with anger and ridicule. But Henoch found
an unexpected ally in Sarah.

"If this is what you most desire," she had said to him, "why
not tell your father that you will only enlist for a limited time,
and that later you will resume your studies, if he so wishes?"

"And will you, too, say a word to him?" Henoch had
eagerly urged.

"Of course. It is natural that a youth of eighteen who has
never been out of this small town should wish to see something of the world."

Accordingly, between the calm arguments of Sarah and
Henoch's fervent pleadings, the Rabbi had reluctantly sur-
rendered. But only on the understanding that the enlistment
should be as short as possible, and that Henoch would resume his studies immediately thereafter. And, although he
would have admitted it to no one, Lazarus was secretly proud
of a son who had the courage to enlist. Also—and on this, too,
he kept his own counsel—it was becoming increasingly difficult to provide for his large family and to lay aside money for
the long periods of study abroad which he deemed so essential to the rabbinical career. Henoch's enlistment would, for
a time, relieve a stringent situation.

So, amidst great excitement among the brothers, Henoch
had departed for the army. He felt rather bitterly that, had
it been a year earlier, he might have known the experience
of fighting under the great Napoleon. As it was, the Allies had
entered Paris in the spring of 1814, and the Emperor had ab-
dicated and retired to Elba. On May 2nd, the House of Bourbon had been restored in the person of Louis XVIII. Henoch
was enlisting under a royalist banner. And who at that time,
least of all Henoch, could have looked a year ahead and have

foreseen the return of Bonaparte and his final eclipse at Waterloo in June of 1815?

To any keen observer, the rather different reaction of the other two brothers to their father's marriage would have been evident. It lay in plain view in the increasing intimacy between Felkel and Jacob. Now that Sarah had created a mutually happy relationship with the two youngest children, Jacob felt free to plan his leisure occupations with Felkel, and in the months that followed the two brothers built up a close comradeship and mutual devotion which were to remain a solace to them throughout their lives. Both were deeply religious. They shared also a love of books. In addition, they had made a mutual and secret pact: that they would never relinquish Samson—that sometime, somehow, somewhere, they would contrive to be near him again.

Least affected by the change in the family seemed to be the Rabbi himself. He was as greatly concerned with the welfare of his children as ever; he remained the stern but affectionate father with the ever vigilant eye, tirelessly supervising their studies and equally determined that each should become a brilliant Hebrew scholar. But it was toward Jacob that his heart leaned most, and upon whom his dearest hopes rested.

The year 1815 would bring, in April, Jacob's thirteenth birthday, and soon thereafter his solemn confirmation in the synagogue as a son of the Law. He spent the preceding months in intensive preparation for this great event. There had been long hours with his father, rehearsing the unpunctuated Hebrew he would be expected to intone publicly—passages from the Torah, and the Prophets. Well he remembered Henoch's performance on his *Bar Mitzvah,* and later that of Felkel. He had considered them very fine—in fact, everyone had said they were—and he must work hard to do as well and not disappoint his father.

Long sensitively alert to the spiritual significance of this milestone, Jacob had for years looked forward to it. As wonderful as had been the early realization that he belonged to the Chosen People, more wonderful still would be this mystical seal that he was acceptable as such. It seemed to him that it would veritably stamp him as a child of God and bring him that much closer to the Eternal Father. As the day approached, he increased his prayers and pondered much on the adult religious responsibilities he would now so gladly assume on this, his spiritual coming of age.

He knew that on that day he would receive the tephillin, those leather straps which ever after when at prayer he would bind to his left wrist, just where the pulse throbbed, and to his forehead; and to which would be attached the small beautiful parchments:

"Hear, Israel, the Lord thy God is one. Thou shalt love thy God with all thy heart, all thy soul, and all thy power." And, "Take my words well to your heart . . . as a sign, tie them to your hand, and as a band between your eyes—write them onto your doorposts and onto your doors."

In addition to a text from Isaiah which he and his father had selected, it had been agreed that he could also recite his favorite selection from Proverbs. To Sarah's fussing about his new, dark suit, he paid little heed; and seemed almost unconscious of the preparation she was making for the feast which would follow, and to which their relatives and friends had been invited, not the least of whom were Banker Schwarz and his son Karl. Jacob had made only one request: that Isaac, the baker, in whose shop on that long ago day he had sought refuge from the sign of the goyim, be also invited. And his father had said:

"Of course Isaac is to be invited. You did not think we would omit so kind a friend, did you?"

At length the never-to-be-forgotten Sabbath morning dawned, a day of late April sunshine. He was up and ready before any of them, and as he waited, trembling with anticipation at the open door, he put his eager young face up to the light, caressing breeze, and was glad that on this, of all days, the wind had come to companion him. For two very dear to him were missing—his mother and Samson.

The Rabbi with Jacob at his side entered the synagogue first, and Felkel with Sarah and the two younger children followed. As in a dream, Jacob was conscious of the number of men who sat on benches against the walls and around the reader's elevated lectern, and he realized that the galleries were probably even more crowded with women—where he had always envisioned his own mother on this great day. The Rabbi, with slow, dignified step, led him to the center of the synagogue. Then he heard one of the seven readers proclaiming his name in loud and solemn tones:

"Jacob Libermann."

(If his knees would only stop trembling!) Then came the cantor's voice inviting him to read from the Law to the assemblage. All at once the trembling ceased, and with a new and strange confidence he approached the tabernacle which sheltered the rolls of the Torah and before which a light glowed—even as one had glowed before that table, long ago, in the church of the goyim.

He faced the congregation, holding the holy scroll. Would his voice obey him? To his great surprise, it did, and the assemblage heard the young voice clearly intone:

"I will mention the loving kindnesses of the Lord, and the praises of the Lord, according to all that the Lord hath bestowed on us; and the great goodness toward the house of Israel, which he hath bestowed on them according to his mercies, and according to the multitude of his loving kindnesses. For he said, Surely they are my people, children that will not lie: so he was their Saviour. In all their affliction, he was afflicted, and the angel of his presence saved them: in his love and in his pity he redeemed them; and he bare them and carried them all the days of old. . . ."

And then: "Who hath ascended up into heaven, and descended? Who hath held the wind in his hands? . . ."

When he had finished, the Rabbi could not conceal the look of joy and satisfaction which suffused his countenance. Ah, not one of them yet, not even Samson (he sighed), not one of them had acquitted himself as well at the *Bar Mitzvah* as had Jacob, his fifth-born. And when the Rabbi began to expound the Law to the congregation, it seemed to many that he spoke with a new force. After the Questions and the Psalms, there followed the blessing of Aaron:

"May the Eternal One bless and protect you! May the Eternal One cast his glance upon you and give you grace! May the Eternal One lift up his countenance toward you and give you peace!"

And the pious Jews of Saverne, turning toward the East and their distant Temple, responded together, "Amen."

Now, on that April day of the year 1815, was young Jacob Libermann established as a son of Israel.

When the men had filed out, uttering their congratulations to Jacob as he lingered on the step waiting for his family, he still felt as though he had been through a dream. Warm were the embraces showered by his own upon him, but when his father approached and took his hand, and said, "Well done, my son," his cup of joy was full.

And because he was loved by all, such a merrymaking had never before been seen in the house of Libermann. He was showered with gifts: Banker Schwarz and Karl brought a beautiful leather-bound writing case from the shop of the widow Schaeffer, and his brothers and little Esther made much of him. As for the feast itself, Sarah, sitting in the midst of the laughter and talk, knew with quiet satisfaction that she had quite outdone herself on the occasion of this celebration in honor of her stepson Jacob, who had today become a true Israelite.

"Poor lad," she thought, "he misses his own mother. Too bad she could not have lived to witness his triumph today. For he is the flower of the flock."

Jacob would have been vastly surprised had he been able to read her mind at that moment. Just then he happened to be listening attentively to his father:

"The next great step will be toward Metz, my son. Prepare well, and when that day shall come, I shall be proud of your Hebrew before the Rabbi Scholom!"

"Yes, Father."

The Rabbi Scholom. He had not seen him since that eventful day when he was five—a day he had never forgotten. An uneasy feeling came over him as he recalled that he had not been very cordial to the bearded rabbi from Metz. But it would be at least seven years more before he would see him again; and perhaps by that time it would have been forgotten.

When everyone had left, Jacob was seized with one of his familiar blinding headaches. But as he suffered it out in silence, a new resolution came to him regarding these old enemies. He would place them in the same category as he would the regular fasting he would now, as a confirmed Israelite, punctiliously observe at the appointed times. For they, too, could be made to serve as "atonement." In that sense, they were good.

CHAPTER FIVE

The Exodus

ON A SPRING MORNING of the year 1822 the stage-coach for Metz, drawn by eight horses, drew up smartly before the Inn of the Three Crowns in Saverne. It had already come a long journey, and while the horses were being changed and baggage stowed aboard, passengers waiting to take their seats observed with interest the distinguished white-bearded Jew of the noble head who was bidding good-by to a slim, sensitive-faced young man of twenty or thereabouts. For so it had been arranged in the Libermann home: only the Rabbi would accompany Jacob to the Inn.

Sarah had hugged him fondly and waved her farewells from the door, and earlier Samuel and Esther had embraced him as they left for school. Samuel, playing the grown-up of eighteen, had tried not too successfully to hide his emotion, and sixteen-year-old Esther had frankly wept.

As two who love each other do at parting, father and son made conversation about practical things when the heart of each was eloquent on far different matters.

"You have my letters to Scholom and Lubinowitz safe in your pocket?" . . . (How I shall miss the boy!)

"Yes, Father. And I shall present them within the hour following my arrival in Metz!" . . . (This is the first time I've left him. He's looking older. Should I be going at all? At one word of his, I would turn back.)

Now as the passengers began to mount, the language of the heart made itself more articulate.

"Remember, Jacob mine, my cloak will fall upon your shoulders. None is more fitting to receive it. So make good time and good progress, that all may be fulfilled."

"My father, how shall I manage without you?"

"It will not be long. And in my thoughts, I shall be ever with you."

A fond embrace; and then Jacob found himself in a rear seat of the coach, craning his neck from the window to wave at the dignified figure who stood there wrapped in the characteristic melancholy of his race. The postillion cracked his whip and the horses were off. For long that glimpse of his father tore at Jacob's heart. He tried to interest himself in the other passengers, but to no avail. The coach was crowded, so he made himself as small as possible in the corner and closed his eyes. It was easier to think this way, and it would be many long hours before they would arrive in Metz. There was much to think about.

Now that the long-awaited day had come, that for which such careful preparations had been made, how would he fare in the city of his destination? It was a much larger city than the one he had always known. He had the advantage of his father's teaching—indeed, it was respected among the Jews of even more remote cities than Metz, even in Paris itself—

so he could not have had better training. But did he himself
measure up? His father's commendation could be attributed
to that of a doting parent for his son. And after all, that of old
Mendelbaum who was not so great a teacher, could easily be
naught but a desire to stand well with the Rabbi of Saverne.

Jacob sighed. When placed in competition with the brilliant scholars from many countries who yearly converged
upon Metz, he might fail miserably. But presently the vital
young spirit lifted itself above such forebodings. He would
try as he had never tried before, would work unceasingly,
and if determination had anything to do with it, he would not
disgrace his father.

Curious, that last talk he had with him the night before.
After supper the two had been alone in the study.

"The Rabbi Scholom has prospered in Metz," said his father. "You will find a comfortable home with him. And it isn't
that you really need the advanced studies there," he continued. "You are already an accomplished scholar. It is not
for these that I send you so far away."

"What then, my father?" he had asked in some amazement.

"In Metz you will encounter some of the greatest intellects,
some of the most famous rabbis, of all Europe. It is for your
acquaintance with these that I send you. I desire that you
should appear well before them. They must come to know
you for as great a rabbinical scholar as you are. For later your
reputation with these can help greatly in your life's work."

Had his father's love overbalanced his judgment? Why,
such words had sounded positively fatuous. That he was to
be "shown off" before the great Hebrew intellects of Europe
as an outstanding scholar struck Jacob as irresistibly absurd.

That dear father! What a fine father he had been, to be sure, to all his children.

He remembered Felkel on a day similar to this only three years ago. Felkel had been sent off to Germany for his studies. That had left Jacob the oldest son at home. He had sorely missed his closest companion, but he and Felkel had managed to exchange weekly letters.

One had to admit that their father had generously and widely spread his sons: Samson to Mainz in Alsace (although later he had made his own way to Strasbourg, the capital); David to Paris, the capital of France; Henoch—here Jacob's mind paused to reflect that Henoch still remained in the army, although it was eight years since he had promised his father to enlist only for a short time. Felkel had been sent to Leipzig —where back in 1813, the year of his mother's death, Bonaparte had been driven to the Rhine. And now Jacob himself was off for Metz, the ancient fortress stronghold of Lorraine.

It had been as though their father had planned that each should acquire a knowledge of differing peoples, toward the end that later in life they could thus be helpful to one another. In the aggregate, the sons of the Rabbi of Saverne would be well traveled. It had not yet been determined where Samuel would be sent, but Jacob was certain of two things: it would be to a city of importance and one whose rabbinical schools were held in high repute.

As though six sons and a daughter had not been enough for any man to rear, there had been two additions to the family since the Rabbi had remarried. Within the past six years Sarah had borne him a son, Isaac; and a daughter who had been named for her mother. So now, of Libermann children, there were eight. Jacob had never thought of the term "half brother" in his relationship with the two youngest. They were as much his own as those with whom he had grown up, even if a good deal younger. So the time would eventually come when even six-year-old Isaac would be sent away for study. If his father should live that long. (O Eternal Father, grant him many years to come, that his children for whom he has worked and sacrificed without stint may bring him honor, and that his later years may be crowned with peace.)

His mind reverted with pain to the two sons who had disappointed the patriarch: Samson, the doctor, and Henoch, the soldier. The Rabbi had borne the defection of Henoch with far less repining than that of Samson, and after all, there was yet hope that Henoch might some day resume his studies. But Samson, the beloved first-born, had married a woman none of them had ever met and had been practising medicine in Strasbourg these past five years. Jacob sighed again. All the more reason that he must prepare himself quickly for the career of rabbi. For in his heart of hearts he wondered whether David and Felkel would ever persevere to the end. They had never been as attracted to the Hebrew studies as had he and Samson. Samuel? He had never been sure, although Samuel, like Felkel, was very religious. As for the new little brother Isaac, it was much too early to tell.

As the coach pitched along over the rough road, his mind again reverted to Samson and Henoch. Since their mother's death, Jacob and Samson had corresponded frequently. And now that he was away from Saverne, surely there would be an opportunity of visiting Samson in Strasbourg. But he must be careful not to offend his father.

In regard to Henoch, an amusing thought struck him. For some time there had been conscription in Alsace, and only a few months ago Jacob had just narrowly missed being swallowed up by the army through having drawn a "lucky number" in the draft. Every tenth name registered was automatically released, and purely by accident, he had been "Numero 110"! He had frankly rejoiced that his rabbinical studies would not be interrupted by a term in the army, but he could not help smiling to think how disappointed the army-minded Henoch would have been, had it happened to him.

What a wonderful thing it would be if all the brothers could foregather for a reunion around the familiar table at the next Passover, a year hence! Perhaps—perhaps within that time, the Almighty would be so merciful as even to permit him to bring about a reconciliation between Samson and his father. And Jacob, somewhat wearied by the excitement of the past few days, and as the coach was now traveling over a smoother and more ancient road built centuries earlier as only the Romans knew how to build, rested his head against the back of the coach and dropped off to sleep.

It was odd that a dream he had not known since he was a very little boy returned to him that day, there on the journey. Again he was alone in a small boat. It was the same dark, rough and tempestuous sea. Then appeared, afar off, the bright light approaching nearer and nearer. Would it rescue him? Then in the center of the light there appeared a cross, and upon the cross there hung the figure of a man. . . .

When many hours later the stagecoach entered the ancient stronghold of Metz, it was through the Port d'Allemagne, that marvelous castellated structure which had been built in 1445 and which yet bore traces of the siege of Charles V. Jacob was immediately struck by the quaint antiquity of the buildings and by the apparent vastness of the town. He was amazed to see so many people on the streets, and the whirl of traffic on the roads dizzied him. But his heart leaped within him as he reflected that here, in such a city, he would learn much, not only from books and history, but from life itself. Why, all these hurrying people, old and young, were his brothers and sisters—yes, he secretly believed, even those who were goyim. He felt drawn to all by an indescribable tie. And a great surge of gratitude to his father welled up within him.

After the stage had stopped before an inn on a thickly populated street, somewhat stiff from the journey he stepped inside with his heavy portmanteau to make inquiries as to the whereabouts of the Rabbi Scholom's house. Learning that it was on the other side of the city and that he must engage a carriage, he was greatly disappointed. He had expected to walk, as he would have walked in Saverne. His father had provided him with money but he knew that he must expend every centime carefully. There were so many persons over whom the good father's money must be made to stretch. But perforce he had to ask a boy at the inn to find him a convey- ance. The one soon produced was drawn by a plump white horse and driven by a rotund, good-natured German who seemed not at all dismayed by the competing carriages and carts that rattled about them, nor by the narrow, tortuous streets through which their route lay.

Presently they came to a bridge which crossed an arm of the river Moselle, and Jacob learned from Fritz, his driver, that the city was built on both sides of several such waterways which were crossed in all by fourteen bridges. Learning his way about Metz would be complicated.

He felt for the letters within his pocket. Actually, but for the addresses they bore, he did not really need them, for his father had written to both his friends a month ago apprising them of Jacob's arrival on this approximate date. Both had replied that they would be glad to welcome him. To be sure the Rabbi Scholom, who many years before when a student in Saverne had made his home with the Libermanns, had neglected to mention that he would expect Jacob to stay under his roof. But his father had assured him that this was merely an oversight, since through the years such an agreement had frequently been mentioned in correspondence between the two.

Tired and travel-stained as he was, he would be glad to reach the house. Presently they passed an imposing Jewish synagogue, and after rounding another corner Fritz drew up before a substantial, well-kept dwelling. Jacob noted that it was almost twice the size of his father's house in Saverne.

"Shall I wait?" asked the driver as the young man paid him from his precious store of coin.

"Oh no, I am expected."

"Good day, then," said Fritz, flicking the whip over his horse's broad back.

As the carriage disappeared down the street, Jacob lifted his portmanteau and mounted the steps. But before he had time to raise a hand to the large brass knocker, the door opened from within. A maid-servant, obviously on her way to some errand, seemed startled by the appearance of the stranger on the doorsill.

"I am Jacob Libermann from Saverne," he explained. "I would like to see the Rabbi Scholom."

The woman looked flustered.

"He is away," she answered. "He has gone to Leipzig."

"Oh! When will he return?"

"Not for a fortnight."

With a great effort, Jacob managed to stammer:

"Did he not leave some word about—about me?"

She shook her head stubbornly.

"But surely—he knew I was coming—"

The woman looked at him sharply.

"What did you say your name is?"

"Jacob Libermann, of Saverne."

This time she shook her head more vehemently than ever.

"He is away, I tell you. He will not return for a fortnight."
And she turned to close the door behind her.

Just at that moment a door within the house was heard to
open. Voices of two men in conversation came to them on the
steps.

"Don't come to me with such a story as that!" cried one
harshly. "I was not born yesterday!"

"But, Rabbi—"

The two were now in the hall approaching the front door
which the maid's hand, as though paralyzed by fear, had
failed to close. Talking angrily, the Rabbi was about to show
his visitor out. Upon the instant he caught sight of Jacob, he
paused.

Not quite knowing what he was doing, Jacob addressed
him:

"The Rabbi Scholom?"

"Yes."

"I am Jacob Libermann, from Saverne."

Scholom cast a furious glance at the trembling maid whose
mouth was wide with consternation. Then he turned upon
Jacob one of the smiles which after all those years Jacob still
recalled with distaste.

"Ah, yes. I remember you as a rather spoiled youngster. Well, you must excuse me today. I am very busy."

There was an awkward pause as the first visitor, discomfited, passed down the steps. The terrified maid plunged after him. Rabbi Scholom stood there, eyeing Jacob coldly and without inviting him to enter. The boyish face of the slim young man flushed, and he shifted awkwardly from foot to foot. Then he pointed to the portmanteau.

"I—I have no lodgings," he stammered.

"Oh. Well, you'll find plenty of them just across the bridge." He waved vaguely in the general direction from which Jacob had come. "Almost any of those houses on the water front, they all take lodgers."

And with that he turned abruptly and closed the door in Jacob's face.

Humiliated as never before, Jacob picked up the portmanteau and descended the steps. There was outrage and indignation in his heart as he turned distractedly down the street. Within a few paces he came upon the first visitor, a middle-aged Jew with an amiable face who was obviously waiting for him. He fell into step beside Jacob.

"A hard man, the Rabbi Scholom," he remarked.

"It would seem so," agreed Jacob.

"You are a stranger in Metz?"

A lump came in Jacob's throat.

"Yes."

"Well, he's not the sort to help a stranger. Had you known him before?"

"He—he used to live with my family in Saverne. He was a pupil of my father's."

"Oh? Your father then is a teacher?"

"My father," said Jacob, lifting his head, "is the Rabbi of Saverne."

"Oh, oh! And Scholom received you thus?"

Humiliation and bitterness poured from Jacob's lips.

"He permitted my father to believe that he would welcome me, that his home would be my home, even as ours had been his. And he knew I would come on this day. My father notified him. Yet he had instructed his maid to say that he was out of town."

The man eyed Jacob with compassion.

"What a pity! But his heart is very hard. Come now. Be of better cheer. Surely you have other friends here?"

"One," confessed Jacob in a dispirited voice.

"Well now, *one* can sometimes be worth *ten!* Come, let me help you find him."

Jacob rested his portmanteau on the street and drew out the two letters. One he carefully tore to bits, dropping the pieces disdainfully into the gutter. The other he handed to his new acquaintance.

"Herr Abraham Lubinowitz," he read. "Why, he is the well-known rabbinical scholar! Now, that's better. But his house lies at some distance. And one cannot hail a carriage hereabouts."

The two paused uncertainly in the street.

"I'll tell you. Leave your bag with me," said the stranger. "I live but a few paces away. You can return for it later."

Jacob hesitated.

"But—but suppose he invites me to stay with him?" he asked.

The stranger noticed the ring of hope in the young man's voice.

"Ah, that is true. Well, perhaps you had better carry it with you then. But it's a long walk. So take it slowly."

Jacob thanked him with warmth.

"Come to see me," said the stranger, "when you are settled. I live just there." He pointed to a small shop with living quarters above it. "I'm Tannenbaum, the tailor."

Jacob's smile was full of gratitude. And the cheerful tailor, having given him directions, disappeared into his shop, leaving him to lift his burden and proceed on his way. As he walked along, he began to feel baffled and lonely in this strange, overlarge and overbusy city of Metz. Moreover the insult he had so lately received stung his sensitive nature cruelly. Plodding wearily onward, he wondered which was the heavier—his heart or the portmanteau. When his wounded and fluttering thoughts had again reached a basis of sorts, he found that his heart was heavy, not so much at Rabbi Scholom's cold rejection as at the bold affront leveled at his father. That was outrageous. Was the Rabbi of Saverne not held in respect by the Rabbi of Metz? But that was absurd. All the Hebrew world respected his father. To him, Rabbi Scholom owed all his knowledge, and his very position in Metz. But for Jacob's father, he would not now be a rabbi.

Worse than all that was the fact that he had been treated as a son by the Rabbi of Saverne, had been made one of his family, had partaken of his bread and slept under his roof for years. All as a gift. Yet he had not so much as inquired about his father's health. Jacob told himself that his instinct about Rabbi Scholom had been right, after all, even at the age of five. How then could his father have been deceived? Perhaps because Scholom had been one of his first pupils and had in truth been a good scholar.

Then in his mind there arose the disquieting question as to how he would inform his father that he had not been received at the Scholom home. That would be difficult. For he would not have his father's feelings outraged. He would not have him made unhappy, or concerned about him on this, his first exodus from home. In handling this situation he would have to be every inch a man—every inch of his twenty years. But how to do it? There was the further matter of expense. Unless Lubinowitz should offer him shelter—and no such arrangement had been made—he would have to ask his father to increase his allowance in order to pay for lodging and food.

His mind fretted with the problem, tossing it back and forth as he crossed the bridge over which he had so recently been driven with a comforting sense of security, and which now on foot not only seemed ten times as long but also found him with a most unhappy sense of insecurity.

The house of Abraham Lubinowitz lay in an ancient quarter of the city, and was itself ancient. For Lubinowitz was a scholar who loved the great things of the past, as Jacob was to observe when after an hour's weary tramp he was ushered, hot and dusty, into a small wainscoted reception room of the sixteenth century. It was furnished with exquisite French pieces of that period. Herr Lubinowitz was at home and would see him at once. This was better, thought Jacob, as gingerly he sat down on one of the frail, beautiful chairs.

Presently there entered a little bent old man, slight of stature and white-bearded but with a magnificent head, deep-set eyes of great intelligence, and a thin, finely chiseled face. There was warmth and charm in his greeting.

"The son of my old friend Libermann!" he cried, holding out both hands in welcome.

Jacob had risen instantly.

"Sit down, my dear Jacob, sit down. You are indeed welcome. Your distinguished father and I have been friends these many years, since we were students together. Tell me, he is well?"

"Very well, thank you, and sent his affectionate greetings to you, as well as this letter." Jacob drew out the missive.

"Good!" exclaimed his host as he opened the envelope and read the message with obvious pleasure, nodding his head the while in approval.

"Ah, I understand. You are to make your studies at the school under my direction, and the Rabbi Scholom at whose home you will dwell—"

Jacob flushed and interrupted him softly:

"Pardon, sir, I'm afraid there has been a misunderstanding about that. I have just come from the Rabbi Scholom's house, and it seems that he cannot receive me."

The ancient's white eyebrows went up in surprise.

"No? Well, that is too bad. What will you do?" The old man seemed genuinely distressed. "I cannot, alas, take you in here; the place is too small, and my widowed granddaughter and her boy occupy the only space I have."

"It is very kind of you," said Jacob quickly, "even to mention it. I only thought you might recommend me to some modest lodging where I could be near the school."

"Ah, yes. That I can do. Near the school, and near me as well—for you must come often to us for meals."

For the first time since his arrival in Metz, Jacob felt he was welcome. His heart warmed to the kindly old man. Very shortly Lubinowitz was questioning him about his knowledge of Hebrew and the studies he had covered in Saverne. Modestly Jacob tried to tell him, and at each admission which the ancient drew from him, his host seemed the more pleased.

"Ah, excellent! Your good father has trained you well, and also you seem to have a natural aptitude, my son."

As he spoke he was thinking what a winning smile and gentle manner this young man possessed. And all the while his shrewd old eyes were gauging the intelligence marked on the broad forehead and latent in the alert brown eyes, which despite their alertness held something of the dreamer and idealist—and yes, perhaps also of the mystic. Here was a pupil worth having.

"Hearken, my son. I will take you at once to a house where some of my students lodge. I believe, to our good fortune, that a room was left vacant only yesterday. They are simple quarters and reasonable in price, but you will find congenial companions there, and also one or two teachers, I believe. Metz, as you no doubt know, is full of schools, students, and teachers."

"So my father has said. It is very kind of you, sir."

"Not at all. But just one word of caution. While only Hebrews dwell in the house—the good widow Kafritz is the landlady—not all the inmates are Orthodox. Some, I fear, have strayed widely from the ancient faith and customs. You will be careful then to consort only with the Orthodox."

"I will be guided entirely by you, sir."

"That is wise, for you are far from home. And now we will start. You will be anxious to rest and refresh yourself after the long journey."

It was a good three days before Jacob could summon the courage to write to his father. With the resiliency of youth and a night's sound sleep his fatigue had vanished and the alert brain had reasserted itself. Truth was the only method to pursue with his father. In fact under any circumstances, every fiber of his nature rebelled against a lie. Even to save the feelings of those he loved, he had never been able to lie. But now, in his letter, he would soften the truth. He would omit the circumstances which indicated that Scholom had left instructions that Jacob was to be turned away at the door. He would merely say that the Rabbi could not receive him as a guest.

Then he would dwell at length upon the gracious welcome extended by Herr Lubinowitz, and his kindness in finding him a lodging and starting him on his studies. He would explain that he would need more money than had been anticipated, but would also relate the careful plans he had made to live within the strictest economy in order to lessen as far as he could the sacrifices which were being made for him. But after the letter had been dispatched, Jacob for two days had a series of his blinding headaches. In addition, he was homesick to the core.

The Rabbi of Saverne possessed keen eyes to read between lines. Moreover, he knew his Jacob. His rapid reply was one of fierce invective and anger against Rabbi Scholom, but at the same time full of gratitude to his old friend Lubinowitz and of solicitude for his son. Jacob must not worry. The money would be forthcoming. He was only to study much and gain a reputation for scholarship among the great Hebrew intellects of Metz. And his father's blessing was upon him.

When that letter came Jacob felt greatly relieved. And now he began carefully to plot his course of study and to survey the circumstances in which he found himself. The house of the widow Kafritz lay conveniently near that of Lubinowitz and also the Israelitic school he would attend. But it was a poor, run-down affair, scuffed by the feet of many decades of students. Upon his arrival the widow had shown him a room on the second floor with a pleasant window overlooking a garden, but had named a price which to Jacob seemed fabulous.

"I will not have very much money," he had explained shyly in his soft voice. "Is there something not so fine that you could let me have, at less cost?"

The widow's attitude—full of graciousness at the start when the famous Herr Lubinowitz had presented Jacob at the door and left him with her—changed immediately. She surveyed Jacob with a cool contempt.

"There's a room in the attic," she had grudgingly allowed, "at something lower than this price. But you will have to fetch and carry your own water, up and down stairs, and there's no fireplace."

Jacob had seized upon it and found that it sufficed. There was a small window high up in the wall through which at night he could see the stars. There was a simple bed which was as hard as the floor, but the linen was snowy white. He had a long table with a lamp for writing and space for books, two stiff wooden chairs, a chest, and a stand with pitcher and basin. Moreover he had a neighbor, judging from the sounds which came from the next attic room to his. His meals he would find elsewhere as best he could.

His introduction to the Talmudic school was a happy one,

sponsored as it was by the highly respected Lubinowitz. (To Jacob's relief he soon learned that Rabbi Scholom did not teach in this school, but in one on the other side of the city near his own synagogue. He hoped that he would never encounter that Rabbi again.) Here, then, with some eighty students who haled from almost every country in Europe, he plunged with enthusiasm into the higher rabbinical studies. Jacob's facility with French and German which he had learned to speak in his bilingual Saverne, coupled with his attractive personality, soon won him good friends. But he shunned intimacies, feeling that he could not indulge in leisure occupations which would absorb time from the work he hoped to accomplish and from the exacting religious program he had laid out.

However, he thoroughly enjoyed the not infrequent occasions when invited to partake of a meal at the home of his father's old friend. That little household shone in an aura of deep spirituality and rigorous adherence to the Law, and in this respect was so like his own home in Saverne that it served to soothe away much of the homesickness. In addition, it brought a new and fascinating stimulus in its devotion to art, and for the first time he began to experience aesthetic joys as his host talked brilliantly about the fine pictures, ceramics, and furniture with which the little house was ladened. Occasionally, too, there would be music, for Frau Weber, the widowed granddaughter, played delicately upon the spinet. Fortunately also, their synagogue was not the one over which Rabbi Scholom presided, so Jacob's religious devotions were undisturbed.

But spontaneously as had arisen an affection for the kindly old man who had stretched forth hands to help the unhappy stranger, it was not long before Jacob began to discern a quality of mind in his elderly friend that distressed him. It was odd that one who could be so kind, who was so deeply religious, possessed of a sparkling intellect and almost a tenderness for all inanimate things of beauty, could be so hard toward his fellow men. Jacob began to notice it in a hundred little ways. It was not alone in the traditional condemnation of the goyim—that was to be expected—but it lay in a harsh attitude toward those of his own race who failed to follow the strict Orthodoxy.

Against these his fury knew no bounds, and more than once Jacob had painfully observed episodes in the school in which his secret opinion was that Lubinowitz had been flagrantly unjust. Would not this, Jacob asked himself, drive those with somewhat liberal views even further away from Orthodoxy? And he was constantly warning Jacob against the enticements of the "learning of the goyim," with the temptations toward which he said the city was rife.

To quiet his mind when it had sheltered what he considered disloyal thoughts against his elderly friend, he would go home to his attic room and write a long letter to Samson in Strasbourg, with whom he was now in regular correspondence. Samson had been delighted to learn that he was in Metz, and filled his letters with good counsel on how to live economically in a big city, a feat which Samson, through much hardship, had early learned for himself. He also wrote charming bits about his wife and her distinguished Jewish family, and described at length his work as a doctor, in which he was totally absorbed. By a sort of unwritten agreement between the two, the letters of each spoke little of Jacob's rabbinical studies. Samson's defection in that respect revived too many unhappy memories. Jacob's letters were full of enthusiastic descriptions of Metz, for the only leisure he permitted himself was his long walks in the evening through the fascinating old city.

He wrote his brother of the ten city gates which through the centuries had been strongly fortified, and how Metz had been termed *La Pucelle* because she had never been invaded; from earliest history she had repelled her enemies. He had heard that the Romans had first called the settlement "Mediomatrica," of which the word Metz finally became a contraction. And a student had told him that Caesar had described it as one of the oldest and most important towns in Gaul. He would like to read Caesar but, as Samson knew, the study of Latin was forbidden.

The Romans had fortified Mediomatrica and constructed a great aqueduct, parts of which still remained. Moreover, they had built the road leading to Strasbourg, only ninety-nine miles distant. He hoped soon to travel over that road to visit his brother. In the thirteenth century Metz had acquired the privileges of a free imperial town, and in 1648 had been ceded to France by the Treaty of Westphalia. This long history had stamped the city indefinably; and each quaint bridge, each antique building, and every narrow winding street drew Jacob irresistibly. They were silently eloquent of the drama of vanished centuries. He yearned to know more.

There was, he wrote, a most beautiful Gothic cathedral whose earliest stones had been laid in the thirteenth century. But he did not confess to his brother the wild temptation, against which he had thus far successfully struggled, to enter it and view the interior.

One evening as he was writing just such a long letter to

Samson, he suddenly found he had exhausted his supply of paper. He was greatly disappointed as he had wanted to complete the letter before going to bed. Searching among his books for a stray piece which might be lurking there as a marker, he heard the door of the other attic room open, and the steps of his neighbor within. The thought struck him that perhaps this gentleman whom he had encountered several times on the stairs, and who always gave him a pleasant word, might be kind enough to lend a piece until he could return it on the morrow. He would not like to ask a student, but his neighbor was middle-aged and obviously a professor—a plump jolly little man with a merry eye. The urge was so great to finish writing to Samson what was in his mind, that he overcame a natural reluctance to trouble others and knocked at the door.

"Come in," urged the pleasant voice.

Jacob shyly entered. "A thousand pardons," he said, "I wondered whether you could be so kind as to lend me just one piece of paper to complete the letter I am writing to my brother?"

"Why, of course. But come in and sit down while I get out my portfolio."

With one of his characteristic smiles Jacob sought a place to sit. It was difficult because the only two chairs were piled with books, as was also every other piece in the room. He perched on the window sill, and while the professor was rummaging among the volumes and papers on his table, Jacob gazed about him with delight.

"May I look at some of your books?" he asked timidly.

"But certainly. You are a student here?"

"Yes. In the nearby Talmudic school."

"Ah. Well, I am a teacher, but not in that school. I teach classes in Greek and Latin at the university."

"Oh, that is Gentile, is it not?"

"Yes, but we have some Jews there also, including myself. Not Orthodox, of course."

The professor had dug out a well-worn leather portfolio, and from it drew several pieces of note paper.

"Here. You are most welcome to these. And don't even think of returning them. I never get time to write any letters myself."

Jacob extended a grateful hand.

"It is wonderfully kind of you."

"Not at all. Ah, I see you were looking at the Plato *Dialogues*. Do you read Greek?"

Jacob fondled the book, and sighed unconsciously.

"No," he said. "As learning of the goyim, it is forbidden."

"You are Orthodox, then?"

"Yes," said Jacob simply, "my father is the Rabbi of Saverne."

"Oh, I understand." And then after a pause, "Just the same, it's a great pity you don't read Greek. Why, you are missing vast treasures!"

The professor's voice took on an even pleasanter quality. His kindly gray eyes lighted up with enthusiasm. Taking the book from Jacob, he opened it at random.

"Here, for instance. Just listen to this."

With one hand stuck behind his back beneath his coattails and the other holding the volume aloft, the professor struck an attitude and rolled out the majestic Greek passages. Jacob was immediately fascinated.

"Beautiful! But what does it mean?"

"Translated, it says: '. . . what men in general term peace is . . . only a name; in reality every city is in a natural state of war with every other, not indeed proclaimed by heralds, but everlasting. . . . All men are the enemies of all other men, both in public and private, and every individual of himself.' "

"Oh, sir, may I write that down?" asked Jacob eagerly.

The professor laughed delightedly.

"Of course. But here—not on that letter paper. You're going to need that. Here's a piece that will do."

He handed Jacob a scrap from his table and dipped a quill in the ink. Then he dictated the passage slowly to his excited guest.

"I suppose you don't know any Latin either?"

"No, sir, but I have often thought how much I should like to read Caesar for his descriptions of Gaul. Here in this city one is reminded—"

"Precisely," interrupted the professor. "It's a great, great pity that you are so restricted. For I can see that you possess a liking for study. And what good, all that Hebrew, if you cannot companion it with other ancient tongues?"

Jacob sighed again. "It is the Law," he said simply.

"Bosh!" exclaimed the professor. "Excuse me. Let me say that I was brought up that way, also. But it didn't take me long to find out how criminally stupid it all is. How it chains the intellect! It keeps a man bound within a chicken coop, and with no chance of developing more intellect than a chicken possesses."

Jacob gazed at him in wonderment.

"You really think so?" he asked.

"I know it. Come now, I suppose you can't read French?"

Jacob shook his head.

"I speak both French and German," he said, "for they are the tongues used in Saverne where I grew up. But it is also forbidden to read them."

The professor's scorn reached a new crescendo.

"Now, isn't that ridiculous? As though a man could call himself educated and move about the world at all, and yet be unable to read French and German. Why, it's an outrage! I'm so indignant at the way you are being cheated that I'd like to undertake your instruction myself!"

"Oh, sir, that is very kind! But you see—you see—"

"I understand. Your father—"

"Yes. But just the same, I'm very grateful to you. And I hope you will let me serve you in some fashion, since we are neighbors. I would be very glad to do errands for you."

"Thank you, young man. I will remember. By the way, my name is Joseph Titescher. What's yours?"

"Jacob Libermann."

"Well, Jacob, drop in to see me now and then. And if you ever change your mind about the Greek, just let me know."

An hour later Jacob was still finishing his letter to Samson.

"I have found a good neighbor," he wrote. "He read to me from Plato that peace is only a name, that every individual is the enemy of himself. How true that is! And he thinks that the rabbinical training keeps a man bound, as he said, inside a chicken coop with no chance of developing more intellect than is possessed by a chicken."

To which, and much to Jacob's infinite surprise, Samson shortly after replied, "I agree with your neighbor."

It was a thunderbolt to Jacob. Of course he was intimately aware that Samson had forsaken Hebraic studies for medi-

cine, but he had no idea that he had lost all respect for them.
Poor Samson, how tragic it was! How deep had been the cut
made by the goyim upon his soul!

More determined than ever to make amends to his offended
father for Samson's defection, Jacob threw himself with a new
fervor into the traditional studies. Six months had slipped
away, almost without his realizing it, and by now, despite his
modesty and shyness, he was recognized as one of the most
brilliant students in the school. He was by all odds the favorite of his teachers. For he was the only excellent student they
had who had not developed, along with his scholarship, a
certain unpleasant arrogance. Jacob wore his skills gracefully,
almost carelessly, as a cavalier of old might wear his cloak.
Lubinowitz was delighted with him and lost no opportunity
of claiming him as a protégé.

But now it became evident to Jacob that much of the
ground he was covering in the school was extremely familiar.
Almost all of it was matter that he had covered with his father
in Saverne. He realized that his father was a greater Hebrew
scholar than many who taught here and were held in high
esteem. And with this realization the inevitable happened.
He began to grow bored.

He no longer found it necessary to spend long hours in his
room, poring over the Hebrew texts. A great many he already
knew by heart. Of course one could go on, over a lifetime,
with the Talmud, fishing up this point or that point, and
painstakingly comparing the interpretations, but for some
strange reason he seemed to have lost all zest for this. He was
frankly chilled with boredom, and as naturally as a leaf
reaches for the sun, the keen young mind began to reach out
for warmth.

For long he struggled with the temptation, and then one night, able to withstand it no longer, he rapped at his neighbor's door.

"I've come, sir," he said somewhat tremulously, "to ask you about the Greek. If you could lend me a beginner's volume—"

He got no further. The professor was on his feet and had flung his arms about him.

"Hosanna!" he cried joyfully. "You won't be sorry. I'll teach you myself, in the evenings."

"But," objected Jacob, "I have no money for lessons. My father sends me just enough for the school. I thought I might study a little by myself—"

"You don't need any money," exclaimed Titescher. "It will be a pleasure to start you. And as we go along, you will find that gradually you can do a lot by yourself."

So it was agreed, the professor promising to keep it all a secret, for, as Jacob explained, both Lubinowitz and his father would be beside themselves with anger.

Then did the young mind begin to experience such intellectual pleasure as it had never dreamed, for Titescher was a dynamic teacher whose enthusiasm for his subject was the essence of contagion. Jacob could hardly wait for the alternate evenings when the two sat over their books in the professor's room. On the other evenings he studied by himself, and thus it came about that there were always two or three of the professor's volumes in his room.

It was not long before his teacher suggested that they should vary the diet with a little Latin, to which Jacob happily assented. After a few more weeks French was added. In deep gratitude to his mentor, who seemed to have dropped from heaven, and in order to make his voluntary task easier, Jacob began to steal daylight hours also for these studies and correspondingly to neglect his Hebrew.

But not a day passed that he also did not feel severe qualms of conscience. He was deceiving his father. It was as clear and as blunt as that. Jacob's mind had a characteristic of going directly to the point. It did not beat about the bush or quibble with side issues or wander off on vague hypotheses to lead him to weak excuses. He was conscious that there was only one basic fact. He was deliberately deceiving his father. Accordingly, he knew hours of intense suffering. But he found that to give up the new delights he was tasting was beyond his strength. Besides, had not the professor said—had not Samson written—? But that was not the point. The point was that he was deceiving his father.

But since God was all wisdom, and knowledge was the gateway to wisdom, why was it wrong for a man to aspire to wisdom through knowledge? Would he not be a better rabbi for having a better knowledge of the world and its people? But again, that was not the point. He was deceiving his father.

These agonizing periods of conflict became so intense that he fell ill. For days he lay on his bed, moaning and tossing under the weight of the monstrous headaches which now beset him. Every night the professor would tiptoe in, bearing a jug of fresh cold water, and would lay a cool compress on his head as he jested the while to him in Greek. Jacob could eat nothing. But as he grew better he was again drawn irresistibly toward the forbidden fruit. For it was an absorbing world which was being laid open, piece by piece, before his fascinated eyes. As for the professor, he was delighted. Not for a long time had he encountered as quick and as receptive a mind as this.

Not long after his illness Jacob was sitting alone in his room one evening with a French grammar laid open before him on the table. It was very quiet in the house, for the professor had not come in yet and all the lodgers were out for supper. Jacob had eaten early in order to have a longer evening with *les verbes irréguliers*, which were proving a challenge. Presently he heard steps on the stair. He lifted his head and listened. They did not sound like the professor's. They were slower, as though made by an older person, and they seemed uncertain, as though pausing to seek their way. Gradually they approached his door, guided no doubt by the light from the lamp which gleamed beneath it.

Jacob was seized with an unaccountable depression. Then came the knock. He rose hastily and opened the door, expecting to see a stranger, come to inquire for some other lodger. But to his amazement there stood Herr Lubinowitz.

"Ah, Jacob. I thought I would give you a little surprise. I was out for a stroll and was passing. I recalled that your room is on the top floor."

"Come in, come in, Herr Lubinowitz," cried Jacob joyfully. "This is a great honor. Never before have you visited me, yet I have been so often in your beautiful home."

He tossed the books from a chair and led his visitor toward it. His elderly friend sat down and looked about him.

"Well, it is not very large," he commented, "but I can see that it suffices. And the air from that window is good. But it is chilly here." He pulled his cloak closer about him.

"I had not noticed. I'm sorry. May I place my cloak over your knees?"

"No, no, thank you. I cannot remain long, for I see I have interrupted your studies. I half expected I would find you out for supper."

"I had supper earlier than usual," explained Jacob. "There was some special work—"

He stopped abruptly and flushed.

"Ah," said Lubinowitz, eyeing him keenly. "I should like to see it."

And before Jacob could utter a word he had risen quickly and approached the table, throwing the young man into utter panic. For there, sprawled out in plain view, lay the French grammar.

Slowly Lubinowitz picked it up and surveyed it. What seemed to Jacob an eternity of silence followed. At length, with a gesture of abhorrence, the old scholar flung it violently across the room. Then he stooped to examine the other books that were strewn about.

"So," he said finally, with infinite scorn, "the learning of the goyim! It has come to that! You have betrayed your father and your friend. You have betrayed your religion. You have betrayed your God!"

The old man rose to his full height and thundered at Jacob like an avenging prophet. With hands raised in repudiation, he cried:

"I denounce you. From this day forward you may no longer look to me for friendship and guidance. For I warned you. And you will no longer be welcome in my home. I have wasted my time on you; for, after all, you are no more than scum. And I shall seriously consider, young man, whether I shall write to your father!"

And with that the fiery old man thundered out of the room and down the stairs, uttering imprecations as he went. Jacob, quivering from head to foot, flung himself face down on the bed—and for all his twenty-one years, sobbed bitterly.

CHAPTER SIX

The Darkness

NEVER HAD JACOB felt as lonely as in the months that followed. Even when his mother died, he still had been left with those about him who were, after her, his dearest upon earth. But now, far from his father and brothers, a black desolation possessed him as he realized that the last remaining human link with home had been abruptly and finally severed. First, the Rabbi Scholom; and now, Herr Lubinowitz. His father's only two friends in Metz had repudiated him. He felt completely alone, adrift upon a friendless and uncharted sea.

There had followed upon the visit of Lubinowitz a period of self-imposed solitude when he prayed much for guidance, in the synagogue and in his attic room, and sat alone for hours debating within himself the questions which were troubling him. For he must come to a decision, and that by himself. Should he renounce these studies as any conscientious Orthodox Jew of that epoch must? Should he follow implicitly the Law as interpreted by his father; by Mendelbaum, his early teacher; and by Lubinowitz, his mentor in Metz? Or should he foreswear their precepts and follow the promptings of his own common sense, and those of Samson and his new friend, Titescher?

It seemed to Jacob that this marked the first important decision he had been called upon to make for himself. He experienced all the suffering common to young people when a beloved oracle whose decisions have hitherto been accepted unquestioningly appears suddenly shorn of infallibility.

Worst of all, a blight had fallen upon what had been his greatest solace ever since he had come away—his communication with his father. Now he never lifted pen to write him without apprehension and constraint. And in opening the letters in response he was never free from the same emotions. For Lubinowitz had departed with the threat of apprising his father of Jacob's willful breach of the Law. Had the old scholar fulfilled this threat? Jacob had no means of knowing, for since that catastrophic evening Lubinowitz had not spoken to him. At the school he passed the young man with averted eyes, and Jacob, fearing that he might even denounce him publicly, no longer had the courage to attend his discourses.

Thus for the first time apprehension hung over his relationship with his father. It clouded an atmosphere that had ever been translucently clear. His natural inclination toward truth urged him to write the Rabbi all about his transgression. But writing was not the way. He needed to talk with him—but he had no money for the journey to Saverne. It was not that he so much dreaded his father's wrath, which he knew would be swift and sure, but rather that he dreaded to bring grief upon the old patriarch. Heretofore he had never caused him the slightest anxiety, and he shrank from doing so now. In his time, he reflected, the Rabbi had been forced to bear much sorrow. If by any human means he could avoid increasing it, he would. Except by renouncing the studies of the goyim. For at length he had determined he could not do that, being now convinced that the oracle was in error. Unhappily he recognized this as the first time he had ever considered his father in error about anything. And as a result the misery of his lonely heart sank to new depths.

There are few trials in life so hard to bear as uncertainty between two who love. And now Jacob lived under the constant uncertainty of how much his father knew. Was it only imagination which construed the Rabbi's recent letters as being somewhat colder and more aloof in tone? Had Lubinowitz really informed him and his father decided to say nothing for the time, perhaps waiting for Jacob to make his own confession? The young student could not guess, and accordingly his days were miserable.

Nevertheless, the decision made, he returned avidly to his Greek, his Latin, and his French; telling himself that one day, when he had become a rabbi, he would have no opportunity to pursue these and that he should make the best of his time now, while they were still available. But he also eased his conscience with a new and determined assault upon the studies offered by the Israelitic school.

Apart from the blissful oblivion to all other concerns which study had always afforded him, his days were unhappy and lonely, and offered their only solace in his frequent correspondence with Samson. Increasing the gloom of his situation was his poverty, for the allowance from home was pitifully small, prices in Metz were rising, and frequently he went hungry to bed. But not a word of this would he permit to creep into his correspondence with his father.

One day there came a letter from Samson which brought cheer to his brother for the first time in weeks. Samson and his wife had a child! Jacob rejoiced with them and replied that now perhaps Samson's breach with their father could be healed, as surely the Rabbi would be delighted to learn that his first grandchild had been born. But Samson remained curiously silent on this point. It was something which distressed Jacob and threw him into a new period of depression.

He had not yet been able to undertake the expense of a trip to Strasbourg, as dearly as he had longed to go. Try as he would, the fees from home barely covered his mere subsistence. He was impatient with himself that he could not do what Samson had done when in a worse state. When totally cut off from funds, Samson had gone forth and earned a living as a teacher, paying for his studies to boot. But Metz was full of teachers. Small chance Jacob would have in that field, and there was none other in which he could qualify.

It was all the more remarkable of Samson that in the face of grave difficulties he had not only wrested a living and a dignified career, but had also achieved a happy marriage and a child. His oldest brother was indeed a great man. Jacob longed to meet his wife, for over the years the letters from Samson had revealed her fineness, her loyalty and her complete devotion. It had first been proved when, upon their falling in love, her family had strongly opposed the match as unsuitable to one of her social status. She was the youngest daughter of the faithful banker of the Elector of Hesse, William I, who when the French invaded their land during the Russian campaign had persistently refused to hand over to them the property and goods "of his princely lord." For this the French had retaliated by burning one of his estates and a nearby forest, causing Babette's father to die of a broken heart.

Loyalty ran in her blood; and she had been loyal to Samson throughout the six long years when the impoverished tutor was struggling to attain his medical degree, and this in the face of stern family opposition. They had met in Mainz not long after Samson's father had cast him off, and it was actually the young man's distress which had brought them together. For the medical student had obtained employment as a private tutor to the young children of the wealthy Reinach family, and in this home lived Babette, the charming eighteen-year-old sister of Frau Reinach. Samson had written that it had been love at first sight. She was four years younger than he, and was deeply religious. She had prayed and sustained his courage throughout the long betrothal, assuring him that once he had obtained his degree as a doctor, the opposition of her family would melt. And so it had. Unstinting labor had won Samson a brilliant standing in the final examinations—so good, in fact, that he had at once been offered an honorable medical position in Strasbourg. So Babette and Samson had been married—in a synagogue and before a rabbi—and with the good wishes and blessings of the bride's family. And they had taken up their residence in Strasbourg.

Of late Samson's letters had avoided all mention of religion, and his younger brother was troubled. About this time a friend of Samson's passed through Metz, bearing an introduction to Jacob. He was a Jew about Samson's age, and conducted a flourishing business as bookbinder in Strasbourg.

Samson's love of books had led him to this shop and the two had become fast friends. So it was that Samuel Klotz made it a point to send a note to his friend's brother upon arrival in Metz, with an invitation to dine.

When the message reached the lonely Jacob in his attic room, it seemed to him that the sun had momentarily broken through the dark and heavy-laden clouds. He was to talk with someone who knew his Samson intimately—who had seen him but yesterday. Moreover they were to dine in one of the city's better hostelries. Poor Jacob had not had a nourishing meal in weeks.

After much animated conversation through the early part of their dinner, during which Klotz had assured him of Samson's established position, of his notable work and his happy family life, Jacob drew courage to ask his host whether Samson remained faithful to the Orthodox religion. Klotz hesitated a moment before he answered.

"Well," he said finally, "he never misses synagogue on the important days."

"That is good news!" cried Jacob, smiling happily. "His work throws him so constantly with the goyim that I had wondered."

"I'll tell you a curious thing," said Klotz, mellow with the good wine they were served, "that caused me to wonder also. Not long ago several of us took a day's excursion into the countryside. It happened that at a crossroads we came upon a Christian shrine. There it was, in all its horror—the cross, the naked man nailed to it. Samson stopped suddenly and gazed at it for a long time. And do you know what he finally said?"

Jacob shook his head apprehensively.

"He said," continued Klotz, meditatively twirling his glass, " 'It is a sublime thought that a God should die for men. If I could only believe it!' "

Jacob was shocked into a moment's silence. Then he frowned and said:

"Yes, it is a sublime thought, but it is one based on a colossal falsehood! Oh, my poor Samson! I hope—"

Klotz interrupted with a reassuring laugh.

"Oh, don't be concerned. No need to worry about one who attends synagogue as faithfully as does your Samson."

And so Jacob had returned home somewhat reassured, but not before commissioning his host with many messages and asking him to carry to the baby a little carved wooden toy which he had purchased at the cost of two of his precious francs in a neighboring shop.

Apart from this episode, the year 1823 passed dismally enough for Jacob. It is true that the brilliant, jolly professor remained his neighbor and teacher, but, as was natural, his heart hungered for a friend of his own age. Then just toward the close of the year, on a cold December day when he sat shivering in his icy room trying to study—he could not afford a charcoal brazier such as made the professor's room cozy— Jacob found a new friend. Unable longer to endure the frigid attic, he had reached for his well-worn cloak, and taking along his book, had gone out. The outdoors, for all the snow, would be warmer, and if he could not find somewhere a spot of winter sunshine, then he would go to the cheap near-by tavern frequented by the students, where he would order a glass of wine. That would entitle him to a table and permit him to study, even if amidst a noisy din. The tavern would be warm.

Finding the outdoors quite as cold as his room, he rapidly made for the inn and ensconced himself near the great roaring fireplace. He had barely ordered the wine and opened his book, when a pleasant voice asked:

"Would it trouble you if I were to sit at your table? The place is crowded, and—"

Jacob looked up to see a young man of about his own age. The face was both intellectual and merry.

"Certainly," said Jacob, reaching for another chair. "Come and sit on this side. It's nearer the fire."

Gratefully the stranger sat down. He also carried a book. The two looked at each other and smiled.

"Too cold to study in one's room," observed the young man.

"It is," agreed Jacob.

"I only arrived in Metz the other day. My lodging, which is anything but warm, lies not far from here."

"Mine as well," answered Jacob; and told him where he lived.

"Why," exclaimed the stranger in surprise, "that is where I also lodge!"

They both laughed at the coincidence. The innkeeper approaching, the stranger ordered a glass of wine for himself, and overriding Jacob's protests, another for him.

"You see," he explained, "it's pleasant to talk with someone. I don't know a soul here. I haven't spoken to anyone but our landlady in the past three days."

Jacob's heart warmed to him. He knew how that was.

"My name is Jacob Libermann," he said.

The other looked his amazement.

"And mine, Lazarus Libmann!" he exclaimed.

At this further coincidence, with names so nearly alike,

they both went off into peals of laughter. Between laughs, Jacob was finally able to stammer:

"And my father's name is Lazarus!"

"Now come," said the new Lazarus, "it is all too much. We live in the same house, your father has my first name; almost you have my last name—and I suspect that we attend the same school!"

It transpired that they did. Then there was nothing for it but that they should have another glass. This time Jacob attempted to pay, but his new friend would not permit it.

"My father has given me plenty," he said, "and desires me to make friends."

It further developed that Lazarus had come from a town in Alsace not far from Saverne, where his father was a successful merchant. By the time the two had their supper together and started for the house of the widow Kafritz, they were friends, for it had been revealed that Lazarus shared Jacob's religious views and was a keen student of Hebrew. He was also here in Metz to study law.

When they parted, they enjoyed the last laugh of the evening, for Lazarus paused before the door of the room on the second floor which looked out upon the garden.

"In finality," said Jacob with a grin, "this was almost the room I myself engaged. Good night, Libmann!"

"Good night, Twin Libermann. Until tomorrow!"

Not in a long time had Jacob retired with such a light heart. Thereafter the two were much together, and Jacob delighted in taking his new friend for long walks through Metz, acting as guide to all the ancient places he had discovered for himself. His friend's interest in history equaled his own. Best of all, he found him completely sympathetic on the subject of his new studies.

"After all," said Lazarus, "many of the strict Orthodox would bar the study of law also; and here I am in Metz especially to prepare for a legal career. How think you I could do that, had I not studied Latin and French? My father—"

"Ah, but you see *my* father is a rabbi," interrupted Jacob.

"True. And you should be every bit as proud of him as you are. But even so, nothing should stop you from now gathering all the knowledge you can. When you come to be a rabbi yourself, you will need it."

Jacob was far more advanced in Hebrew than was Lazarus, and so was able to help his light-hearted friend greatly with his elementary studies at the Talmudic school. . . .

It was a far better new year than he had anticipated, thought Jacob, shortly after the dawn of 1824. Why, talking with Lazarus was almost as satisfactory as talking with Samson or Felkel! Regularly the two friends attended synagogue together, and usually followed this with a long walk and a discussion of religion. They found themselves agreed on the beauty of the ancient rituals, on the magnificence of the Psalms and the Prophets, but little by little, as they discussed and argued, notes of doubt about the Talmud and its interminable interpretations crept into the conversation of each. Both confessed what they would not have admitted to any other—that in the present century many of the strict, detailed religious observances seemed pointless, although they understood thoroughly the historical reasons which had prompted them. And both loved best the Prophet Isaiah, who spoke of the "loving kindnesses of the Lord"; and least, those who had spoken of His wrath and revenge.

"Take for instance," said Jacob one day, "the 'eye for an eye, and a tooth for a tooth.' Why, even my most Orthodox father has never acted upon that principle." And he told Lazarus the story of how he had cheated the merchant, and what his father had said.

"Your father is a holy man," replied Lazarus, "but do you know what the goyim teach on that point?"

Jacob was incensed.

"How should I know their religious teaching?" he demanded.

"Oh, come," said Lazarus, "a little knowledge of that won't hurt you, any more than their Greek and Latin. Now I'll tell you, for I heard a law student explain it the other day. In such circumstances as you describe, in which a small lad thinks he has done well by cheating a merchant and tells his righteous father about it, the father would make his boy return the franc as not rightly his."

Jacob was silent. He had to admit to himself that his father had not gone that far. And as his mind reviewed the situation, he was forced to recognize that the other teaching on this point was superior.

"Don't let it worry you," said Lazarus. "Precious few of the goyim live up to what they teach. For every Jew who cheats one, there are a hundred goyim who cheat the Jews. Why, just look at what they have done to us, down through the centuries. The exiles, the confiscations, the Inquisition, the pogroms!"

"Agreed," said Jacob sadly, "and to God's own Chosen People."

It was not long after this conversation that Lazarus, who

loved to prowl about the secondhand bookstalls of the city, one day brought a volume to Jacob.

"I was looking for something in Hebrew," he explained, "to give myself more practice in reading. And I came upon this for a mere song. But the only trouble is, the text is unpunctuated, and I'm not yet able to read the unpunctuated Hebrew. I wondered if you would help me?"

"Of course," said Jacob, taking the worn leather volume and opening it. "Why, this is the Christian Testament!"

"I know," said Lazarus, "but it won't bite you."

Jacob laughed and sat down with the book. Lazarus pulled up a chair beside him. They began at the beginning—the Gospel of St. Matthew. But after a little, as Jacob read aloud, Lazarus began to fidget.

"It all sounds to me very dull," he interrupted, "all that genealogy. Besides, I've a lecture to attend at the law school. I'll leave the book with you. Perhaps you'll come upon something more interesting." And he was off.

The hours passed, and Jacob did not stir, except to turn the pages. Forgotten was his discourse at the Talmudic school. Forgotten too, that he had eaten nothing since early morning and that dusk had come on. Forgotten everything, but the book on his lap. . . .

It so happened that he did not see Lazarus again until the next morning.

"How did you make out with the Christian Testament?" asked his friend.

"Oh, I read most of it; and when you're ready, we'll go at it together again."

"And your impression?"

"Why, it's rather amazing. Very beautiful and lofty, in places. But the account of that man's miracles! Absurd. Old wives' tales. And the assumption that he was the son of God horrifies me. Blasphemous!"

The following day there came a letter from home. Jacob opened it with his customary trepidation. But his father wrote in the same general vein as usual, only now there was no longer any doubt that the letters were colder and more formal than they had been when Jacob first arrived in Metz. This missive did, however, contain a piece of news. Samuel had been sent off to Paris to complete his studies. David, who had spent several years there, had returned home shortly after Jacob had left for Metz, and he was now assisting his father in the Saverne synagogue. He had urged the Rabbi to send Samuel to Paris, not alone for its superior Israelitic schools, but also that he might have the advantage of friends in the higher Jewish circles whom David had known there.

These tidings indirectly reminded Jacob that he had been neglecting his own Jewish studies; and as though to cleanse his mind from the effect of the New Testament, he now undertook a new and thorough reading of the Jewish Bible. To his dismay, he found that something strange had happened. Passage after passage which he had always accepted unquestioningly filled him with doubt. Some even repelled him. He told himself that this was only a temporary phase, that he would soon pass through it, and that probably he was tired— were not the headaches which had assaulted him during the past few days proof of this?—and that the exalted faith he had always felt when reading the holy book would soon return. He would say nothing to Lazarus. But as the weeks passed, the doubts, rather than lessening, only increased. With them came a veritable agony of soul.

Despairingly he hastened to the synagogue, alone and in secret. There he prayed imploringly, day after day, and frequently not without tears. But doubt and darkness only deepened about him. Could this be himself, Jacob Libermann, the devoted son of the holy Rabbi of Saverne? Little by little he reviewed his childhood and boyhood: his lovely, pious mother; the truly spiritual father; the joy he had known on the religious feasts in that Orthodox home; the momentous occasion of his *Bar Mitzvah*. He tried with all his soul to recapture those moments of exaltation, when he had felt himself almost to be in the presence of God. To no avail. All was dry and barren. It was as though he were wandering in a desert place. Odd, that the only flashes of peace which came were when, quite irrelevantly, one of those passages he had read in the forbidden Testament would obtrude itself.

That one magnificent discourse: "Blessed are the poor in spirit . . . Blessed are the meek . . . Blessed are the clean of heart. . . ." And what was that passage written by the man they called John? "He came unto His own; and His own received Him not." Ah, that *did* tear at his heart. For Jacob himself knew something of such an experience. Had he not, in Metz, "come unto his own"—to his father's friends? And his own had received him not. Few experiences in life could be as bitter. Involuntarily his heart went out to the Nazarene. Yet what a strange figment of falsehood the whole thing was. Those miracles; what credulous fools were they who believed them! And the body and blood of this Jew, to be eaten, to be drunk—revolting, monstrous!

But now the miracles in his own Bible appeared equally revolting. That God should stoop to such absurdities! Then it was that the darkness descended overwhelmingly like something flung from above, enfolding him utterly. All was totally black. And Jacob Libermann no longer believed. . . .

It was fortunate, he told himself, that Lazarus had gone home on a visit, for he would never have been able to conceal his unhappy state—and not for anything would he have disturbed the faith of his friend. Insofar as so sweet a nature could feel superior, he was even a little patronizing in his thoughts. Lazarus was happy in his ignorance. Let him remain so. Perhaps by the time he returned Jacob would be more accustomed to the darkness and would be able to dissemble.

As Lazarus would pass close to Saverne on his journey, Jacob had given him a letter to his father, cautioning him however not to mention his new studies or the liberal conversations the two had shared in Metz.

"Above all," begged Jacob, "try to find out if he is well. Notice everything about how he looks, and bring back to me a detailed report. You might throw out hints to learn whether he intends to let me come home soon; for the truth is, Lazarus, I long to see him."

As he waved his friend off, his heart was heavy that he could not go with him, yet he smiled so gaily that Lazarus never guessed it. Then feverishly he had begun to seek new books which only led him deeper into the darkness.

When his friend returned a fortnight later, there was so much to hear and to question concerning the visit to Saverne that the subject of religion for the time remained dormant in their conversations. Eagerly Jacob had awaited his return on the appointed day, and had kept his door open so that he might hear from below the traveler's steps. When they sounded, he flung himself down the stairs and greeted Lazarus joyfully.

"Come in," said the smiling Lazarus, as he led the way into his room, "and hear all about it."

He threw his portmanteau in a corner, shoved Jacob into a seat on the bed, and began:

"Your grand old father, but he is magnificent! Never have I seen one who is so nearly a replica of what we dream of the Prophets!"

"But how is he?" pressed Jacob.

"He seemed in the best of health, vigorous of mind and body; labors long every day in the synagogue, and in his study. He received me most kindly, as did your stepmother— they pressed their warm hospitality upon me—they could not do enough to make me feel welcome."

Jacob smiled happily.

"Did—did my father ask about me?"

"Now, why should you be interested in that?" teased the other.

"Please!" begged Jacob.

"All is well, little one," smiled Lazarus. "He inquired at length about your health, your lodging, your clothes, your food, our pastimes—and of course he asked if you were getting on well with your studies. But not a word did he say about Greek and Latin!"

"The Lord be praised," sighed Jacob. "And Esther? And the two little ones?"

Lazarus had started to unpack. His back toward Jacob, he paused a moment before replying.

"All thriving," he finally said. "Your sister Esther—"

"Yes?" pressed Jacob.

"She is very beautiful," murmured Lazarus as he bent over the portmanteau.

Jacob's eyebrows went up. Then he asked carelessly: "You think so?"

"The most beautiful Jewish maiden I ever saw—the loveliest—the most virtuous!"

"Ah," said Jacob mischievously, "you wouldn't be falling in love now, would you, Lazarus?"

From the depths of the portmanteau Lazarus heaved a profound sigh. "I'm afraid so," he murmured.

Jacob flung his arms about him.

"Splendid!" he cried. "And of course she loves you?"

"I don't know," mourned the other. "That's the worst of it!"

"Well, we'll just see to that," announced Jacob in a big-brother tone.

"Of course, I was prepared to love her—for after all, she is your sister—but only as a brother, you understand. But I never expected to feel this—this—" He paused for lack of words and looked so woebegone that Jacob rolled over on the bed, laughing.

"Oh, my poor Lazarus!" Then he sat up and said seriously: "I'm delighted. Of course she loves you. What girl could help it?"

"Do you think—do you think—I could speak to your father?" asked the other anxiously. "I'm not worthy of her—"

"Nonsense! It would be an excellent match for Esther. You are of suitable age, of good family; you will be a lawyer, and you will live not far from Saverne. You are Orthodox—" He stopped abruptly.

"Oh, I will ever remain Orthodox, if Esther will only have

me!" cried Lazarus excitedly. "And 'her people shall be my people,' and so on."

And thus more than ever was Jacob estopped from revealing his inner spiritual misery to his friend. Meanwhile he continued to attend synagogue and the school as though nothing had happened. He had determined to wait for the darkness to vanish, as he felt sure it eventually would. For the time, he would disturb no one. But alone in his room at night, he lay awake for hours and came face to face with a soul that was bleak and desolate. . . .

For some time the letters from Samson had been so sparse that Jacob began to be anxious. Long weeks went by with no word from him. When at length a letter would come, it was brief and constrained. What was happening to Samson? Was there family trouble? Was there business trouble? Then one day, late in the year 1824, a thick letter arrived. Jacob was just leaving the house for a session at the school when the post was delivered, so he seized the letter and stuffed it into his pocket until he could be alone in his room. For somehow he was certain that it contained important tidings. Once in the school he found that he could not keep his mind on the discourses at all. The letter hung heavily against his chest, depressing him like some unrevealed grief.

At length able to hasten home, he ran up the stairs quietly lest Lazarus should hear him and come out to interrupt with some plan for the evening. Softly he closed the door of his attic room and took out the letter. Seated where the light from the high window could best reach the pages, he began to read. Suddenly he sprang from his chair as though shot from a catapult. He walked up and down, involuntarily moaning and holding his head. For the quiet pages now lying strewn upon the floor spelled out a great tragedy for the house of Libermann. Samson, the first-born, had not only become a Christian, but had joined the most pernicious of the sects. In fine, he had become a Catholic.

"You have no idea, my dearest Jacob," he wrote, "what happiness possesses me and Babette! Such peace as you cannot imagine—after the long years of wondering and doubt. At last we feel as though we had 'come home.' . . . It all happened several months ago, that is, when we and our baby were baptized in the Catholic faith. But I delayed writing to our father, knowing that he would be deeply disturbed. At length I feel that I can no longer withhold the news; so accordingly a letter goes to him today by the same post which carries this to you."

Jacob sat down at the table and held his head in his hands. His father—the Rabbi of Saverne—his splendid old father, would be completely broken by this news.

"If only I could go to him!" he moaned aloud.

Then with trembling fingers he picked up the pages and read on. It seemed that Samson had for long passed through a great interior darkness. As he described it, Jacob recognized it as similar to the one he himself was now experiencing. Then one evening when he and Babette were visiting neighbors who were Christians, Samson had idly picked up a book in their home. It was part of the Protestant Bible, the New Testament. ("That is odd," thought Jacob, "for I too happened upon the same. But it did not change *me,* as it has my poor Samson!")

He continued reading: "Babette and I took the book home with us, and read it through aloud. When we had finished, we were completely convinced that this was indeed the New

Law—that Jesus of Nazareth was in truth our Messiah, and the Son of God."

Jacob felt suddenly very sick and had to lie down on his bed. It appeared from the letter that for many years, in fact even in the far-off days when they were engaged, Samson and Babette had ceased to believe in the Orthodox faith of their fathers. Together they had discussed their doubts and had begun to read many books which for a time had led them into complete agnosticism. But that their families should not be disturbed, they had agreed between them to be married according to the ancient Jewish rite. And for long they had continued to attend synagogue regularly, even punctiliously, each praying quietly in his or her own way—Samson frequently in tears as he implored for a return of the old faith which had brought so much beauty and peace to his youth.

In his profession as a doctor, Samson had been thrown constantly with Christians. "I would have been blind indeed, my Jacob," he wrote, "had I continued to see these as we were brought up to see them. . . ."

"Oh, my poor Samson!" cried Jacob aloud. "How have you been led astray! Have you forgotten the harvest festival at Beaumont, and those cruel words thrown at us—that we were 'the sons of Jewish dogs'?"

There was only one explanation. Worldly ambition had done this to Samson. His career as a doctor . . . he was anxious to get on . . . he had a wife and child to support . . . there was such widespread and unjustified prejudice against God's Chosen People. Monstrous, that his brilliant Samson could debase his intellect to the level of accepting the fantastic story in the Christian gospel. Alas, their poor insulted father! Would it, Jacob wondered, cause his heart to break

—would he perhaps even die from the shock? Samson at least might have refrained from disgracing him. It was the disgrace that would hurt most. Why could he not have kept his unbelief to himself, as Jacob was now doing? But before all the world, openly to join the goyim—a Catholic! After all, their father was the Rabbi of Saverne.

His head began to throb painfully. He went over to the little stand and bathed it with cold water. Then, his heart aching, he picked up the pages and sought out Lazarus for solace and counsel. . . . But for all the other's kindness and sympathetic grief for his stricken friend, Jacob was awake all night with one of his worst headaches.

Within a few days came the letter he expected—and dreaded. His father's sentences were grief-laden and disjointed; and here and there Jacob thought he saw a trace of tears on the pages.

"The entire family here," he wrote, "has put on the garb of mourning for the son who is now dead to me—and as a brother, dead to all of you. I expect you in Metz, Felkel in Leipzig, and Samuel in Paris to mourn him as though he were even now in the grave. I am writing the same to Henoch."

The next day Jacob shut himself in his room to write the long letter to Samson he had been composing in his mind ever since the thunderbolt had fallen. In it he expressed his utter amazement that Samson's keen intellect could accept the old wives' tales of the new gospel. He pointed out fallacy after fallacy. But mainly he dwelt upon the insult and disgrace to their good father and the name of Libermann; and for the first time in his life he reproached his beloved Samson. The letter which Samson sent in return completely disarmed him. The older brother had taken no offense. On the contrary, his message breathed only gentleness and love. And patiently Samson had tried to lay open portions of the Christian creed.

In return, Jacob at last unburdened himself to Samson. Yes, he could understand how the ancient faith had ceased to hold him; for indeed, for several months now, he himself had been beset by doubts. Those miracles, for instance! Why had a God who was just and loving performed such world-shaking miracles for those early unworthy Israelites who repeatedly fell into sin and paganism; and yet the same God did not lift a finger today for the suffering and abused, holy Jews all over the world, who adored the One God, and who lived, bereft and forlorn, in righteousness? His "Chosen People"! There was no sense to it!

To which Samson replied patiently that it was but another proof that Christ was the true Messiah. For, he explained, now that God had sent His Only-Begotten Son to earth, bearing the richest of miracles to mankind—the Eucharist, the Sacraments—and now that the Son had laid down His life for the redemption of mankind, there was no further need for the Father to work the stupendous miracles of the past for His erring children. They had but to turn to Christ.

Jacob shook his head in utter negation. He tried going back to the Talmud—but it was of no use. Yet he must regain his faith! Otherwise, how could he ever become a rabbi? He could not fail his father in this; above all now, when Samson had planted this cruel knife in the loved breast. Yet how, in his present state, could he ever become a rabbi? Desperately he sought out the synagogue and prayed for a return of faith. But still nothing but darkness surrounded him. He could only wait. . . .

It had not taken Lazarus long to find another excuse for a

visit to Saverne. He returned from it full of sympathy for the sorely stricken Rabbi, and even more in love with Esther than ever. For her part, he had reported to Jacob, she had seemed less timid with him, and while they had not yet seen each other alone, he had drawn courage from the smiles she had shyly bestowed.

"Soon," he confided to Jacob, "I shall make another visit, and this time I shall speak to your father."

"Excellent!" cried Jacob. "It will take his mind off his trouble. There's nothing like a new trouble to take one's mind off an old one."

Lazarus looked utterly crestfallen. Jacob laughed and flung an arm across his shoulder.

"Come! I was only teasing. My father will actually be pleased. Only hurry up, and get the agony over with. I'm tired of hearing the sighs and moans of an uncertain lover."

It was not long after this that Lazarus returned again from Saverne the happiest of young men. The Rabbi had given his consent, and so had Esther. Visits had been exchanged between the two families, and in Saverne there was as much rejoicing as could be expected in a house of mourning. Now all that remained was that Lazarus should pass his law examinations—two more long years—and they could be married.

The news helped to lift considerably some of Jacob's depression. The little sister Esther had ever occupied a special corner in his heart. And Lazarus indeed had become another brother. Now too, he felt he could speak frankly with him about the spiritual darkness through which he wandered, for the faith of Lazarus was secured. Not for the world would that one now waver in his Orthodoxy. For was he not affianced to the daughter of the Rabbi of Saverne? And, moreover, madly in love? So Jacob poured out his doubts to his friend, who listened in distress. He could only counsel him to wait and to pray. Samson's conversion to the Catholic Church was all their father could bear at this time. How well Jacob knew that!

"It isn't that I would ever adopt any other faith," explained Jacob. "It's just—it's just about becoming a rabbi—"

"Wait," counseled Lazarus. "And pray. Time changes many things." . . .

Some weeks later there came a letter from Felkel in Leipzig.

"Good news," he wrote. "You recall that I told you some time ago that a friend here had been kind enough to teach me something of the craft of bookbinding in my leisure time? It is impossible to tell you how much it interests me, dear Jacob, and happily my friend assures me that I have made progress, and that now I can do it quite creditably. My friend, by the way, is one of the goyim, a Protestant; and it would be hard to find a finer fellow. (Please say nothing of this to our father, when you write him.)

"In any case, I've been writing Samson about it, and now he has just sent me a letter saying that if I can get our father's permission to transfer my studies to Paris, where I could be with Samuel, there's a good chance that I could soon 'pay my own way.' Samson has a friend, a bookbinder in Strasbourg (he says you have met him) and this kind Herr Klotz has promised to find me employment in Paris with a friend of his who conducts a similar business there. So I am writing to Saverne today to ask permission, explaining that I could soon relieve the household of much of the expense in my regard. But of course I am leaving Samson's name out of it, as in view of his shocking going over to the Catholic Church, it would only cause anxiety. And besides, the two ideas have no connection."

Jacob immediately wrote Felkel his enthusiastic endorsement of this proposal.

"We have all been separated too long. If two of the brothers Libermann can be reunited in Paris, perhaps the rest of us may get there somehow. But Samson seems irrevocably tied to Strasbourg. Oh, Felkel, as dearly as I love him, I cannot recover from what appears to me as black treachery in his giving up the ancient faith."

The next letter that Jacob received from Felkel was from Paris itself. He was happily ensconced with Samuel, was working at good pay as assistant to the bookbinder, and carrying on his Talmudic studies at night. The news pleased Jacob tremendously. If he could only walk in upon the two in Paris one day, how happy he would be! But in Metz, sick at heart with a longing to see his own again, the fifth son of the Rabbi of Saverne battled silently against the blackness of unbelief. . . .

So passed the year of 1825. It was early in the spring of the following year when lightning again struck the house of Libermann. This time it was two-pronged. For out of the blue came the news that both Felkel and Samuel had been received into the Catholic Church. Jacob was stunned. For days he went about as one in a state of shock, oblivious to his surroundings, unconscious of what was said to him. He could not think of his father without weeping. There was no doubt that Samson's hand was in this, even though, as far as Jacob knew, Samson had not visited Paris. But the insidious influence of his letters! And the brothers' carelessness in making friends among the goyim. It was all too terrible. Three of the sons had now betrayed their father. It was like a curse which had fallen upon their house. Henceforth, how much alone he would be in his own family! His three favorite brothers had deserted him.

Each of the two new traitors had written senseless letters in syllables of rhapsody. He still loved them deeply; therefore their folly was the harder to bear. They had even abandoned their ancient Jewish names which Jacob had always loved. Felkel had become "Felix"; and Samuel was now called "Alphonse"—which he was told forsooth, were the names of Christian saints! They were madmen; Samson also. Where was the God of their fathers, to permit this catastrophe to befall? Ah, *was* there any God of their fathers?

He plunged back to his Voltaire; to every book he could lay his hands on; to freethinker, to agnostic, to atheist. In the atheist he found pure reason. Yet while he felt himself to be convinced, he was at the same time miserably unhappy.

And now, cold and without comfort, the spirit of Jacob Libermann wandered desolate and forlorn in desert places. At length something deeper within his soul than could be reached by the reasoning of Voltaire reasserted itself and acknowledged God. But it was not the God of his fathers, nor was it the Christian God. Desperately, he sought a compromise. It would be a God whose only requirement of mankind would be that it should recognize Him, and live in justice and humanity. Thus with a show of assurance he wrote to Samson:

"It makes little difference whether I be Jew or Christian, little difference whether I adore God in a single person or in three. However, I assure you that I would not be a better Christian than I am a Jew. It is on these grounds that I can excuse you for your change of religion." (Ah, how avidly had Jacob sought to find such an excuse!)

But the more he attempted to adjust his faith to a vague deism with a code of morals and ethics loosely pendulating from it, the more he felt that good for the sheer sake of good, like "art for art's sake," was not enough. He thought of the precepts of Plato. Yet man could not live on good alone. There must be something more. But where to turn? If his restless soul could only find peace!

To add to his desolation, the friendly teacher Titescher, his attic neighbor with whom he had been able at periods to forget the agonies of a vanishing faith while plumbing the depths of Horace, of Cicero and Vergil, had left Metz. He had gone to Lunéville, where he had obtained a better position as professor of classics at the college. He had become genuinely fond of Jacob, and Jacob was devoted to him. The two had parted sadly, but with assurances that they would meet again somehow. And the professor had given Jacob three of his prized volumes.

"I will continue the studies faithfully," Jacob had promised. "The Hebrew and the Chaldaic can wait until I return permanently to Saverne. Then there will be plenty of opportunity to master them."

"Naturally," said the professor. But Jacob's long sigh had not escaped him.

With a heavy heart Jacob had returned to his room that night. Lazarus was out dining with some friends from home; Jacob felt unutterably lonely. He had not heard from his father in a long time—the poor old man seemed utterly crushed by his triple tragedy. And Samson's letters had come to irritate him with what he considered their complacency in the insanity which possessed him. There was a volume of Rousseau on his table which he had not yet read, and languidly he picked it up. Some hours later he paused at a certain passage and read it over twice. Then he continued on with the book. It was *Émile*, and in it he was reading *"La profession de foi du Vicaire Savoyard."* But as he turned the pages, this particular passage kept knocking at his brain so often that he was forced to revert to it. It was an exposition of the reasons for and against believing in the divinity of Jesus Christ. After expounding one of the reasons favoring such a belief, Rousseau had written:

"I have not been hitherto in a position to know what a rabbi of Amsterdam would reply to that."

Jacob laid down the book and closed his eyes in thought. After several moments he opened them again.

"I don't see either," he was forced to admit to himself, "what satisfactory answer a religious Jew could make to that question." . . .

The next day he sought out Lazarus.

"Let us go for a long walk," he urged, "for I am desolate beyond all."

His friend gladly consented, and although a light drizzling rain was falling, the two trudged forth. They made for one of the bridges which crossed the Moselle, for not far from the opposite side there was a little park where they had often sat for their discussions. It was a day in late September, and the weather had been as changeable as a coquette's fancy. By the time they had reached the park, the rain had ceased and the sun had come out, drying the benches. They sought a se-

cluded one out of earshot of others. It faced a little lake—
and there the unhappy Jacob laid bare his soul.

"I cannot. It's of no use. I have tried, and I have prayed.
But I can no longer accept the faith in which we were
brought up."

"What then, are you to do? Your studies?"

"That's just it," said Jacob miserably.

"You must give them up," said Lazarus firmly. "At least
those which are preparing you for a rabbinical career. For
obviously you cannot be a rabbi if you do not believe what
you will be expected to teach."

"Obviously," agreed Jacob with a sigh.

"These apostasies of your brothers," went on Lazarus,
"they have vastly upset you."

"Oh, yes! But above all, the grief to my father. And now,
that I must add to it!" He buried his face in his hands.

"I know," said Lazarus, thinking of Esther.

"It's not only all that," explained Jacob, "but something too
that I came upon last night in my reading. Rousseau—"

"Yes?"

Jacob told him about it. There was silence between the two
as Lazarus pondered the question.

"I can't find any answer to that either," he finally confessed. "But if Rousseau, a brilliant and confirmed skeptic,
could not—well, I don't feel so stupid. However, just because
I can't answer it, doesn't mean that I could be a convinced
Christian, only because of that one point. Could you?"

The other failed to answer. Lazarus turned and looked at
his friend in surprise. Finally in a tone so low that the other
could scarcely hear, Jacob said:

"I don't know."

Again a silence fell as they stared out over the little lake. A child was trying to sail a toy boat on its surface, and the two young men watched his efforts as he stooped over it from the bank. Jacob thought: "If only my problem were as simple! How complicated are all problems, once one is grown up!" Over everything there hung a soft September haze and a silence. It was as though they were sitting there in a dream.

Finally Lazarus said:

"There's a very holy man in Paris, a former rabbi who was famous. He too, like your brothers, has become a Catholic—a Monsieur Drach."

"Why, he's a friend of my father's!" exclaimed Jacob.

"And of mine, also," said Lazarus. "Now, if I were you, I would write my difficulties to Drach. He would understand them better than most, because he is a Jew, and was formerly a rabbi, even as your father. He will know how you were brought up. You cannot very well write to your brothers. Their answers could not be as objective as Drach's. And you must go to someone wiser than I for counsel."

"But do you think that Monsieur Drach would pay any attention to a letter from me?" asked Jacob doubtfully.

"Of course he would. He has ever been known as the kindest of men. And I know how you can reach him. On my last visit home, my father told me that he has become a teacher of Hebrew at a Christian school in Paris—the Collège Stanislas, I think he said it was."

Jacob brightened perceptibly.

"Well, it would do no harm to try," he said.

"You should ask him," continued Lazarus, "if you may come to see him. It's all too complicated to resolve in a series of letters."

"Oh, my father would never consent to my going to Paris," exclaimed Jacob.

"He might, if you said that you wished to see what the Israelitic schools there could offer. After all, they're famous. And as loath as I am to say it, it seems to me that you have exhausted the opportunities here; at least for a long time you have been completely bored by the Hebraic studies in Metz. If you really are going on with them, and you may again change your mind and do so, Paris would logically be the next step. Why not write your father and say that you would like to go to Paris?"

Jacob thought a moment.

"No," he said finally, "he would surely refuse. You forget what has happened to Felkel and Samuel in Paris. Also, I fear that my father is already disturbed about me. I'm certain that rumors of my interest in the new studies have reached him. Much better, were I to go to Saverne and ask him myself. Besides, I long to see him. But alas, I have no money for the journey."

"I will give it to you," said Lazarus promptly.

"No," replied Jacob, smiling affectionately at his friend, "but I thank you warmly, just the same."

Suddenly Jacob pulled himself up as an idea struck him.

"I know exactly what I shall do, Lazarus my friend," he cried. "I shall walk to Saverne. My father will then understand how urgent is my desire—"

"Walk? All those miles?"

"Why not? I shall enjoy it," said Jacob, "and besides it will afford plenty of time to reflect on the way. And if only I can persuade my father into it, just think, in Paris, I could see Felkel and Samuel!"

"Splendid!" cried Lazarus. "And in Saverne you could **also** carry my love to your sister."

They both laughed. Jacob's spirits had soared as this plan of definite action took shape. How good it would be to lift the long suspense!

"And I'll tell you what else I can do," he cried joyfully. "On the journey to Paris—that is, if my father will really permit— I can go by way of Strasbourg and see Samson."

"Hosanna!" chanted Lazarus. "Now all our problems are solved, at least for today," he added humorously.

Laughing, the two rose from the bench and started for home.

"Let's go to the tavern and have our supper, and a glass of wine to celebrate," suggested Lazarus.

"Agreed," said Jacob. He was thinking that there was a double reason for going to Paris. If he were not to become a rabbi, he must look about for some means to earn a living, and Paris would offer opportunities.

The next day he sent a long letter to Monsieur Drach in which he outlined his spiritual uncertainty and expressed the hope that, should he gain his father's consent to visit Paris, he might have the privilege of an interview. Drach's response was immediate. He would not only be glad to talk with Jacob, but would see that he would have a room at the Collège Stanislas. There, where he was teaching, they would have ample opportunity to discuss matters. So with heart considerably lightened, if also filled with trepidation over the forthcoming interview with his father, Jacob set off early the next morning on his journey to Saverne.

It was October of the year 1826. As he strode along the highways with a small satchel swinging from his shoulders, he felt happier than he had been in years. How greatly he had missed his father! How good it would be to see him again, and David—and Sarah, and the two young ones, who would have grown considerably in the four years he had been away. As for Esther—with satisfaction he patted his pocket where lay a thick letter to her from Lazarus; tucked within the folds was a little jeweled brooch. Everywhere along the road the autumn foliage was in its glory, dancing under the October sun, swaying to the light breezes. "Who hath held the wind in his hands?" chanted Jacob to himself. Little white clouds gaily chased each other across a deep cobalt sky. What a good idea it had been to walk, thought Jacob. In the stagecoach he could so easily have missed all this beauty.

Yes, he would find changes in those he had left in Saverne. But what of the changes they would find in him? He had left them as a youth, and was returning as a man. He sighed. Would his father be distressed at the change? Perhaps if he knew how much time he had given to the forbidden learning, he would not even receive him. Under his breath he quoted a line that now so frequently recurred to him: "He came unto his own; and his own received him not." So, too, it might be with him, when he reached the familiar old house next to the synagogue.

Why, within recent months he had scarcely touched the Hebraic books! Even if he had heard no rumors, his father would be sure to find out, somehow. Discouraged at this thought, his pace slackened. And how much should he reveal of his spiritual uncertainty? What was that strange observation that Monsieur Drach had made in his letter? He had written that he was persuaded that Christ had already conquered in Jacob's heart! No, that was not true. Probably that could never be. There were those miracles—and many other matters. Once again the darkness closed about him. In any case, he must find out. He must put an end to this misery. . . .

It was a weary and travel-stained Jacob who some four days later knocked one sunny forenoon at the familiar door. His father, in the study, heard Sarah's cries of welcome and came forth to see who it was. For an instant he paused in utter amazement, then flung his arms about his son and wept openly. Leading him into the study, with shaking hands he placed him in the best chair, saying:

"I have prayed that you would come!"

"Why then, did you not send for me, my father?" (How aged the dear one seemed. The deep sorrows and the years had left their mark.)

"I wanted it to be your own wish. And now you have walked all the way! That was wrong. I would happily have sent you the money."

Jacob answered truthfully:

"I could wait no longer."

"Ah, my Jacob, I have been greatly concerned about you. We must have a talk. But come, you are weary from the long tramp, and first you must rest."

He went to the door and called Sarah.

"Prepare his room upstairs. The boy needs sleep." And then turning to Jacob, "Later, we shall talk. And after that, a fine supper, eh?"

Jacob's smile was so replete with happiness that the whole house seemed the brighter for it, thought the Rabbi. That smile had ever been frank, and sweet. Ah, it was too long, too long, since it had warmed his heart! . . . Sarah babbled happily as she led him upstairs. He would see the two children when they returned from school, and would be amazed at how they had grown. By the time he awakened, Esther would be home—she had gone to visit a friend. But it was too bad that only yesterday David had undertaken a journey for his father, but perhaps Jacob could remain with them until his return. She hoped so.

It was a good three hours later when she rapped on his door, and entered with a large steaming vessel of hot water. She poured it into a tin tub, and added a jug of cold water from the stand.

"When you have bathed and are ready," she said cheerfully, "your father asks that you come to him in the study."

Much refreshed from his sleep and bath, Jacob ran lightly down the stairs. He experienced an inner amazement that now that the long-dreaded moment to face his father had arrived, he felt not the slightest apprehension. So it was that with one of his sunniest smiles he entered the study.

"Now, my dear son, I wish first to see what progress you have made in Metz with your Talmudic studies."

("Here it comes," thought Jacob. "If he asks me to recite and interpret from the Talmud, I am lost. For two years I have almost entirely neglected it.")

But that was precisely what his father did ask. Moreover, the question was one of great subtlety, and he knew at once that his answer would reveal all too clearly the degree of scholarship to which he had attained. Jacob drew a long breath and began. Then a very strange thing happened. His mind seemed suddenly illuminated as though by an invisible lamp. The question from the Talmud, in all its obscure and enigmatical aspects, was immediately revealed to him. With the greatest facility he rendered the passage and brilliantly interpreted it. And if the Rabbi had but known, Jacob's surprise was infinitely more acute than was his own. Beaming with joy, the old man embraced him.

"Ah, my dear Jacob, if you only knew what a weight you have lifted from my heart! See." He picked up a sheaf of letters from his desk. "All these have I received, and all repeating the same calumny against you. They have told me that you were neglecting your rabbinical studies, and were wasting your time on forbidden books and learning. How malicious and untrue! For any student who can recite from the Talmud and interpret as magnificently as you just now did, has not wasted his time in Metz."

("O Eternal Father," prayed Jacob, "how can I thank you enough?" For suddenly he knew that in some strange way, supernatural help had come to his aid.)

In the happy conversation which followed, Jacob revealed his desire to go to Paris, saying that he could not feel satisfied about all things until he had talked with his brothers. He had, in truth, suffered doubts. Again, the amazing happened. His father readily agreed, even though Jacob courageously warned him that perhaps the same thing might befall him there as had befallen his brothers. The Rabbi only gave vent to one of his rare laughs.

"After that recitation from the Talmud? Impossible! With all your skill in Hebrew? Out of the question! I will also give you a letter to my great friend there, the good Rabbi Deutz. He will clarify all your doubts and put you in touch with the best masters."

Jacob could not believe his good fortune.

"Moreover," continued the Rabbi, "in Paris I will expect you to bring your brothers to their senses; and in a short time to return to Saverne, prepared to assume the career for which you have been trained."

Jacob hesitated, but something told him that for the time he had said enough.

Then the Rabbi, with his arm across his son's shoulders, led him to the kitchen where Sarah was preparing supper. Out ran the little Sarah and young Isaac to chatter their welcome. And presently arrived the lovely, twenty-year-old Esther to embrace him warmly, and to ask for her dear Lazarus. The Rabbi disappeared into the cellar, and appeared again with a bottle of his oldest wine.

"It is a night for rejoicing," he exclaimed, "for the prodigal son has returned."

Such a supper Jacob had not enjoyed for a long time. He sat at his father's right and next to Esther; and between the good wine that passed, the jolly episodes of Metz that he related which set them all laughing, and the love that surrounded him on all sides, Jacob knew happiness again. . . . Moreover, the long and heavy darkness seemed at last to presage a dawn.

CHAPTER SEVEN

The Dawn

THE FIRE CAST a warm glow over Dr. Liber-
mann's cosy parlor, glistened in shining patches on the substantial walnut furniture, caressed the roses in the rug, and
vied with the flickering candle flames to transmute from brass
to gold the seven-branched candelabra on the mantelpiece.
Outside, the October night had turned frosty.

As Jacob relaxed in a comfortable armchair facing his
brother across the hearth, with Babette and her embroidery
ensconced on a near-by sofa, and with books strewn about in
pleasant profusion, he thought that he had never seen so perfect a picture of domestic peace and well-being.

Following supper, little Agnes Léa, now almost four, had
been put to bed upstairs; and Jacob had been permitted to be
present as she knelt at her mother's knee, and lisped after her
the words of the Lord's Prayer. Although struck by their
beauty when he had happened upon them in the Christian
Testament, he had never imagined they could sound as beautiful as they did now.

Above the small bed there hung a crucifix. Jacob mused that it was just such a sign as this which had struck terror in his heart and beset him with nightmares when he had been about the same age as the child who would now sleep peacefully beneath it. His niece; the granddaughter of the Rabbi of Saverne. Strange. . . .

Her mother had caught the child up, and said:

"Say good night now to your Uncle Jacob."

The small hands had reached up to pat his cheeks as he bent over the fragrant curly head.

"Good night, Uncle Jacob," she had managed to enunciate. "Please stay always."

And then she had been tucked under a warm blanket, clutching the wooden toy he had sent her from Metz three years before. She preferred it to the doll he had picked up for her in Saverne a day or so ago; although the doll occupied a secondary place of honor on the chair by her bed. Jacob had found his small niece completely irresistible. And her name had charmed him. Agnes, for the Christian saint—Babette had told him something of her story—and Léa, for his beloved mother.

Very different had been the journey from Saverne to Strasbourg than the long walk from Metz to his father's home. For the Rabbi had pressed funds upon him with assurances that his allowance would continue to reach him regularly in Paris. So he had traveled by coach, and when a carriage had deposited him at his brother's door, he felt no fatigue. The three happy days at home had restored him completely—but they had also done something else. They had made him certain that if he must deal his father a blow, and the very thought of it made his whole nature shrink, it would be as slight as possible. Perhaps he would have to forsake the rabbinical career, but he must stop there. He would not, could not, add further suffering to the old man's already sadly bruised heart. Monsieur Drach—well, if he never heard again from Jacob, it would matter little.

As he had lifted his hand to the knocker, he had hoped wildly that it would be Samson who would open the door. His visit was a surprise, and he wanted it to be complete. But here he was to be disappointed, for it was Babette who answered his knock. Immediately she had known him.

"Why," she had stammered to the smiling young man standing there, hat in hand, "it must be—yes, of course—you are Jacob! I would know you at once; you are so like Samson."

As she led him in with a gracious welcome and obvious pleasure, she explained that Samson was at the hospital, but she hoped would be home soon. Supper was almost ready; and Jacob must plan to stay the night at least, and longer if he could. How delighted Samson would be to see him!

Then the baby had been led in, and after insisting on a dignified formal introduction, had immediately made herself at home on his lap. A maid was preparing supper in the kitchen, so Babette and Jacob had become friends on that late afternoon, sitting there before the fire. Jacob had found her all and more than even Samson had proclaimed. She had beauty and wit, and her gaiety was contagious. But it was odd hearing this lovely young woman with her definite Semitic beauty speaking quite simply and familiarly of Christian customs. They shocked him, as they tripped off her tongue, for all the world as though she had been born to them, thought Jacob. Once she broke off a sentence to apologize.

"Forgive me, dear Jacob," she had said, "I keep forgetting that you are not yet one with us. Felkel and Samuel—"

It was Jacob's turn to interrupt. He did so with a smile and raised eyebrows.

"You said 'yet,' Babette. Meaning?"

"Oh, it's only a question of time," assured Babette with cool aplomb. "We are praying for you every day, and soon the prayers will be answered."

Jacob laughed; half in discomfiture, half in pleasure. Then he gave vent to a long sigh.

"It's far more difficult than that," he said seriously. "Frequently I wonder if I shall ever have a faith again—in any religion. Spiritual peace seems to lie far without my reach."

"We'll soon fix that," replied Babette cheerfully.

Then Samson had come in, doctor's satchel in hand. He had paused unbelievingly a moment in the doorway, and then had almost bowled Jacob over with his embrace. How they had all laughed and chattered at once!

Now, some three hours later as they sat at the fireside, much of Jacob's recent life had been explained and some of his new plans revealed. But he had strictly avoided all mention of his correspondence with Monsieur Drach. He was going to Paris to consult his father's friend, the Rabbi Deutz; and perhaps to resume his studies there. And he was going to see Felkel and Samuel. At mention of this, he had inwardly resented the rather complacent smile that had stolen across Samson's face.

It had been thirteen long years since the brothers had seen each other, and Samson found it difficult at moments to believe that the eleven-year-old boy who had clung to him on that long-ago tragic day in Saverne had actually grown into this slender, sensitive-faced young man of twenty-four. For his part, Jacob was lost in admiration of his handsome brother, now just beyond the middle thirties, whose face wore the indescribable look of the physician, and whose temples were already tinged with gray. Samson had been overjoyed at his brother's decision to visit Paris.

"I've been praying for that," he stated.

"You and Babette and your prayers!" laughed Jacob. "Surely you don't believe in prayer of that sort!"

"But of course," said Samson simply. "It's more than belief. We know. So I've been praying you into Paris, even as I prayed Felkel there."

"I thought it was Herr Klotz who got Felkel to Paris by securing employment for him with his friend, the bookbinder," teased Jacob.

"And how do you think all that came about, my young friend, if not through prayer?" retaliated Samson.

"But why were you so eager to get Felkel to Paris?" asked Jacob curiously.

Samson did not answer at once but, rising from his chair, began wielding a poker on the glowing coals. Finally he said:

"Felkel had written that he was thinking of becoming a Christian. As all his friends in Leipzig were Protestants, I wanted him also to come into contact with the Catholic Church—for you must know, Jacob, there is only one true church. In Paris, I could arrange to have him meet certain friends."

Jacob looked at his brother curiously.

"I can't imagine why you would go to all that trouble, just to induce a brother to share your faith."

"Ah, but you don't know what it is to be a Catholic! That is, not yet."

"You are as bad as Babette," laughed Jacob. "So you think you are going to pull me in by the hair of my head, do you?"

"Well, not quite that way."

Something deep within Jacob rose in protest. Suddenly he felt violently repulsed by the very thought of Christianity

"You forget," he said quietly, "that our father is training me for a rabbinical career."

There was a moment's silence as Samson, with moody expression, resumed his chair. Babette, sewing busily, broke the pause.

"Samson," she said, "do you not think that Jacob would like to hear more of the story of our conversion? There must be much that causes him to wonder."

And now, quixotically, Jacob suddenly felt a great interest. Samson leaned forward, looking reflectively into the fire.

ity.

"You know," he began slowly, "that Babette and I went you have been experiencing. We know how that is, and it is through a long period of doubt and unhappiness—even as hard. Particularly for you, who have been alone. We were two."

Jacob nodded, not trusting himself to speak. Samson was continuing:

"I'm sure you have secretly wept in synagogue, even as did I—have known all the desolation of grasping at what was once so beautiful and all-sustaining, and finding yourself holding an empty shell."

Then he turned to Babette.

"You take it up from here, my dear," he said.

Babette, with head lowered over her embroidery, continued:

"As Samson must have written you, we had read the Christian New Testament. We were convinced of its truth—and yet we hesitated. It would be such a tremendous change for us! Then one day we knew that we were to have a child, our first."

"Agnes Léa!" exclaimed Jacob.

"No," said Babette slowly. "Before that. We wanted very much to have a son. So we made a vow to the Christian God, that if He would answer our prayer, we would have the child baptized a Christian. We were thinking then of the Protestant Church, to which our good friends belonged. They sent us to a minister. We began the interview with high hopes, but ended it in complete discouragement."

"I don't understand," said Jacob, "I should think—"

"The minister wasn't interested," explained Babette simply. "He pointed out that our child had not yet been born, that there was no hurry to take any drastic step. But what shocked us most was his assertion that baptism was not really too essential. That threw us right back to our starting point. Again we found ourselves without a faith. It was—all black and uncertain again."

"And the child?" asked Jacob softly.

Babette's head drooped lower over her task.

"It was stillborn," she murmured.

Jacob, nonplused, could find no words for the sympathy that flooded his heart. It was Samson who finally broke the silence.

"But behold the goodness of God," he said, "in our little Agnes Léa."

"Yet I don't understand," persisted Jacob, "why, after being repulsed by a Christian church—"

"Again, the great mercy of God," Samson broke in. "It so happened that about that time I was appointed secretary of a Jewish group then involved in a movement to uplift the moral and intellectual standards of our people. One of the first things we accomplished was to have the Jewish catechism translated into German. I worked with two good friends—Mayer, a lawyer, and Dreyfuss, a merchant. But the more we studied the moral problem, the more we were convinced that there was only one way in which it could be solved."

"And that was?" urged Jacob, leaning forward with interest.

"The conversion of all Jews to the Catholic Church."

Jacob dropped back in his chair, feeling slightly ill.

"We decided," continued Samson, "to put this conviction in writing and to send it to the Catholic bishops. I was commissioned to compose the memoir. In it, we proposed the establishment of a society to spread Christianity among the Hebrew people."

"Poor Samson," murmured Babette, "he worked so long and so faithfully at it, and still he seemed destined for disappointment. For the episcopal see of Strasbourg was then empty; and it took a very long time to get the memoir into the right hands."

"Finally," explained Samson, "it reached the newly appointed Bishop of Strasbourg. Bishop Tharin at once sent for us. After several satisfactory talks with him, he asked me to continue the discussions with his vicar-general. Now here is a strange thing: can you imagine his name?"

Jacob looked mystified.

"Libermann!" exclaimed Samson.

"No! Not one of our family?"

"No, but an Alsatian. From Molsheim. I submit that this was even a stranger coincidence than your making a friend of young Libmann in Metz, which has resulted in his being affianced to our sister."

"Agreed. But this Libermann," pressed Jacob, "what—"

"My dear Jacob," Samson interrupted, "it was all very simple after that. Father Libermann, a brilliant theologian, and the soul of sanctity, drew us at once into the Church."

Babette laid down her embroidery.

"And on March 15, of the year 1824, we were baptized; and were born again," she said softly. "God be praised!"

Jacob shifted uneasily in his chair, and turned to Samson.

"What happened to your two friends, the lawyer and the merchant?" he asked.

"Oh, in a very short time, Mayer and Dreyfuss followed us; and then a great many others from the original group—all Jews."

"It's a strange story," mused Jacob. "It would almost seem—" He hesitated.

"Yes?" pressed Samson.

"Forgive me—but it would almost seem like a case of mass hypnosis," said Jacob. . . .

Although his room was warm and comfortable, he did not sleep very well that night. His mind persisted in ceaselessly reviewing the events of this extraordinary day. A change had certainly come over Samson, one deeper than could be accounted for merely by the lapse of years since they had been together. He was—well, he seemed less restless; somehow possessed of a mysterious confidence. His smile came more readily, and his whole manner expressed peace. As Jacob tossed restlessly, hoping for sleep, snatches of Babette's conversation recurred to him. "The child was stillborn. . . . The minister said baptism was not too essential. . . . Poor Samson yet seemed destined for disappointment. He had worked so long. . . . We were baptized, and born again." Born again —what an odd way of putting it!

He must remember, too, what she had said as they had bidden him an affectionate good night:

"If you waken early, and are hungry, you will find a hot breakfast on the stove. I always prepare it before we leave for early Mass, so it will be ready on our return. Our maid does not come to us until later in the day."

They had both protested his determination to take the morning stagecoach for Paris. Why, that would be no visit! But he had remained firm, as deep as was his enjoyment in being with them. For throughout the hours at his brother's hearthside, something within him kept persistently pressing him toward Paris. Of course it was to see Felkel and Samuel— to see the Rabbi Deutz, as he had promised. But to see Monsieur Drach? Ah, no; that he could not do, after all. His father . . . And finally, with a deep sigh, he had dropped off into a troubled sleep.

The next morning dawned cool and crisp, with a touch of frost in the air. As Babette and Samson were returning from church, walking at a fast pace to keep warm, they were surprised to see a familiar figure emerge from their door. It was that of old Ludovic, a crippled veteran of the Napoleonic Wars, who subsisted mainly on the charity of a few neighboring families. But it was in Dr. Libermann's sunny, well-stocked kitchen that he found his surest source of charity.

"Why," commented Babette, "Jacob must be already awake. Else how did Ludovic get in?"

As the old soldier hobbled toward them, he doffed a battered cap and smiled broadly.

"Why, he's got a new cloak!" exclaimed Babette. "I knew he needed one, and was troubled, wondering how we could manage it."

When some five minutes later Babette and Samson entered the kitchen, they found Jacob whistling a merry tune and washing dishes.

"Did you enjoy your breakfast?" asked Babette, as her quick eye rapidly surveyed the dishes and calculated that but one person had eaten.

"Oh, very much," declared Jacob.

"Won't you eat something with us now?"

"No, thank you. I've had plenty."

"Which means, you've had exactly nothing," said Babette severely, putting down the spoon with which she had begun to ladle out the porridge. "We met Ludovic in the street. You had given him a fine breakfast, he said."

"I—I wasn't very hungry," stammered Jacob. "And the old man said you always took care of him."

"True. But there's enough for two guests; and you will please just sit down there next to Samson and eat a proper breakfast."

Laughing, Samson thrust Jacob, who looked like a discomfited schoolboy, into a chair.

"In this house everyone learns to obey Babette," he exclaimed, "especially in the kitchen. Did you think, young man, that you would start off on a long journey without breakfast?"

"Well, Ludovic needed it more than I."

"Just like your cloak, I suppose," scolded Babette. "Of course you have no other. So you had to give it to Ludovic."

Under his sister-in-law's castigation, Jacob felt extremely uncomfortable. Why had the old man been so garrulous? Why were Babette's eyes so sharp? He looked so utterly miserable that Babette was forced to burst into laughter. Eagerly he explained:

"I'm always too warm in a cloak at this time of year. And later, if it's cold in Paris, I can get another."

"It's cold in Paris now," asserted Babette, "and very cold this morning right here in Strasbourg. If you think we are going to permit you to enter that coach without a cloak, you are much mistaken."

"Precisely," said Samson.

"Oh, please no!" implored Jacob. "The coach will be warm, for it will be crowded. And I promise I will get another as soon as I arrive."

And perforce they had to let him go that way; since the doctor himself had but one cloak, and there was no time to make a purchase in Strasbourg before the stagecoach left.

"Come back soon, Uncle Jacob," the little girl had begged, as she patted his cheek in final farewell. Samson, commissioning him with a dozen messages for Felkel and Samuel, had grasped his hand and held it long.

"God keep you, young brother," he said, his voice breaking ever so slightly, and his deep eyes searching those of Jacob.

But it was Babette who uttered the strangest of farewells. Following breakfast, which had begun with a scolding and ended so gaily, she had been silent, moving about her tasks deep in thought, while the brothers conversed. Now at the door, with her hand on Jacob's arm, she had said simply:

"In Paris, all will be made clear. You will not only become a Christian, and one far surpassing us, but—" She had paused for a moment, closing her large dark eyes. Then opening them, and looking up at him intently, she had finished: "But you will also become a priest."

Samson and Jacob were left speechless in amazement. Then Jacob caught up his portmanteau and, with a final embrace for each and a smile, was off. . . .

It was some three days later that a very tired young man alighted in the French capital. He was wearied not so much by the long journey as by the conflicting thoughts and emotions which had plagued it. His father . . . Samson . . . The two visits, coming together so closely and after so long a period of waiting, of hunger for his own, had exhausted him emotionally. For it had so befallen that each of these two dearly loved ones desired of him directly opposing decisions in Paris. He would have to choose: his father and the Rabbi Deutz; or Samson and Monsieur Drach. While within his soul something that stood quite apart from either his father or Samson clamored to be heard in its own right. And Jacob knew instinctively that it was this voice alone that he must eventually follow. In the painful conflict of his emotions and of his inner spiritual doubts during the journey, he had begun to abhor the prospect of what he had so recently and so ardently desired—arrival in Paris. Many times he would have turned back. For he realized that Paris would present the final ultimatum. There the die must be cast to determine the direction of all his future life. Of course the simplest way was to strangle his yearning for God, to embrace agnosticism fully —and to enter a business career.

Miserably he realized that he faced a dark and threatening city whose only beckoning light was the presence of his two brothers. But for that, it is quite possible that he would have dismounted at some stage in the journey, and made his way back to Saverne. "Here I am, my father. I need no further training. Do with me as you wish."

But that extraordinary farewell of Babette's! She was a lovely creature, but a fanatic. Did she think she could startle him into the Catholic Church? Well, he did not startle so easily.

Small wonder then that his first exuberant evening with the delighted Felkel had terminated in one of his most devastating headaches. To his great disappointment he had learned that Samuel, having found an appointment as secretary to a wealthy family, had sailed with them for America only the day before. As Jacob lay on his back in Felkel's modest apartment, it seemed to him that some invisible fiend was chanting a ritual close to his ear. "Deutz or Drach? Deutz or Drach?" ran the endless refrain. But there—he had promised his father to see Deutz; so there was no escaping that.

Felkel at twenty-seven, his senior by three years, had retained many of the boyish qualities and all the natural spirituality which had made him such a sympathetic companion when Jacob's world had turned upside down upon the sudden introduction into the household of a new mother. But Felkel's amazing light-heartedness puzzled him. How could he be happy, realizing as he must the distress he had so recently brought upon their father? Jacob moaned inwardly. Felkel, and Samson and Samuel—three sons. Contemplating the extent of the apostasy, he knew more than ever that for him it must be Deutz, and not Drach. Just as soon as the headache left off its persecution, he would call upon the Rabbi.

But although he deplored the brothers' betrayal, he had to admit the courage of the two recent recalcitrants. For immediately upon hearing of the apostasy, their father had cut them off from funds; just as he had cut Samson off upon his abandonment of a rabbinical career. Fortunately Felkel, making progress at his craft, was now able to support himself. But until Samuel had found his post, he had been forced to depend upon Felkel; and during some difficult months, both had known privation. If Jacob should fail to follow the path indicated by their father, he too could expect to be cut off from funds. In that case, how would he live? Could he find employment? At what? Painfully, and in a fierce, orderly rhythm, his head continued to throb.

Then next day, when he was better, quite incomprehensibly he took a course diametrically opposed to that upon which he had determined. To the end of his days, he was never able to explain that action upon rational grounds. Since his visit to Saverne, had he not told himself a thousand times that while he might have to forego being a rabbi, he would at least for his father's sake avoid getting mixed up with the goyim? Yet here he found himself within two days after his arrival in Paris, knocking upon Monsieur Drach's door.

When the eminent scholar entered his reception room, he faced a very nervous, uncertain young man. But almost at once, his courtesy put the visitor at ease. This man must once indeed have been a very great rabbi, thought Jacob, as he looked into the deep-set, penetrating eyes and surveyed the broad, high forehead. Drach's voice held the rich musical quality so frequently marked in many of his race. And his sympathy for Jacob had been instant.

"At the Collège Stanislas you will have an opportunity to study the questions which have been puzzling you; and we can discuss them as you will. A room has been set aside, and I have already left some books in it. When may they expect you?"

The suddenness of the question left Jacob breathless.

"I—I'm not quite ready yet, sir. I would like a few more days with my brother. Then, too, there is still a commission I must fulfill for my father."

Drach gave him a shrewd glance.

"I assume that your father, whom I admire and remember with pleasure, has not been told of our correspondence?"

"No. Nor my brothers. In fact, sir, I have myself been un-decided about this step, wondering whether I would even meet you. Forgive me. But after I wrote to you, so many new aspects presented themselves, following upon my visit home, and to my brother Samson—"

"I understand," interrupted Drach with a smile.

"And further, you must know, sir," Jacob hastened on, "that I have reached no conclusions. Apart from a belief in God, I am like a ship without a compass, sailing I know not where. It is a terrible feeling. The truth is, I am convinced by neither Judaism nor Christianity."

Drach nodded understandingly.

"I, too, went through all that. It is difficult."

"But it's different with me," cried Jacob distractedly, "for I am the son of a rabbi!"

"And I," said Drach gently, "was a rabbi."

"Forgive me, sir. For the moment, I forgot. But in honesty

I must make it clear upon what grounds I can avail myself of the hospitality of the college. I will go there, if I may, merely to read and to reflect; and to talk with you when you can spare a little time."

"Of course. All is completely understood between us."

Then surprisingly Jacob found himself saying:

"If agreeable to all, I will present myself at the college on Friday of this week."

"Splendid! Come here first and I will myself conduct you." . . .

But Jacob had not walked half a mile from Drach's home before he was assailed by misgivings. . . . "Now why did I set a day for arrival? Why could I not have left everything vague, for the time? After all, I have not even yet called upon the Rabbi Deutz! That I must surely do tomorrow. And that may alter everything."

As he strode along he was conscious for the first time that he wore no cloak. A sharp wind was blowing; and recalling with a smile his promise to Babette, he determined to ask Felkel's assistance in buying one cheaply. He must guard carefully the funds his father had given him. They might, indeed, be the last, he reflected with a sigh.

On the following day, the cloak having been purchased to the brothers' satisfaction, Jacob called upon the Rabbi Deutz. Upon presentation of his father's letter, the Rabbi, of great intellectual charm, received him kindly.

"Your father's letter informs me that you have had some doubts. We will soon put those at rest. They are quite common to normal young people. And surely, you will visit me often?"

"Thank you, sir."

"And now about your studies. When do you wish to resume them?"

"I have only just arrived," began Jacob, "and—"

"Quite. You wish a little time to look about Paris, to settle upon lodgings, and so on. At our next meeting we will make plans for the studies."

"It's very kind of you, sir."

The Rabbi picked up a book from his well-appointed desk.

"I'm wondering whether you have read this?"

Jacob looked at the new treatise on Jewish history which he held out.

"No. But I should like to. Would you be kind enough to let me borrow it?"

"Of course. I believe it may help to settle much that has been troubling you."

Jacob left the charming elderly man with a feeling of gratitude. Here was one who was more nearly like his father than any Hebrew teacher he had met. Ah, if only the Rabbi Scholom had proved to be the same, on that long-ago lonely day, his first in Metz! Would things have turned out differently? He wondered. But he could not help smiling at the irony of life. Now, when he seemed to have passed beyond the need of such a teacher, one was presented; but at a time when most needed, one had been denied.

He had been walking aimlessly, lost in thought, and now he found himself approaching a little park lying close to the Seine. He entered and sought out a bench. It was a golden autumn day; peace lay upon the river and was strewn across a flawless sky. Now the wind arose, sighing through the trees and scattering a heap of gold at his feet. "Who hath held the wind in his hands? . . . What is his name, and what is the name of his son?" Ah, if only he knew! Then suddenly it was made quite clear to him that he would not again visit the Rabbi Deutz—except to return the book after a polite interval of time. But as he made his way back to Felkel's apartment, he thought regretfully of the kindly scholar, and sighed. In other days, here perhaps would have been a helpful friend. But he had come too late.

That night he reflected upon his father's insistence through the years that he should be trained by the best rabbinical minds. In addition to his father, the Rabbi of Saverne, he had been thrown disappointingly with the Rabbi Scholom, pleasantly but briefly with the Rabbi Deutz; and now he would come to grips with the intellect of one who until his apostasy had been famous as the Rabbi Drach. That so distinguished a rabbi could have become a Christian was even more startling than that three of his own brothers had done so. Well, he was willing to explore that mind a little—he hoped fervently that his father would not learn of it—but he was more than half convinced that the exploration would leave him irrevocably afloat upon those vast uncharted seas of agnosticism whose chilling winds were already and unhappily all too well known to him.

The Collège Stanislas was even then an ancient institution. And now for six years it had embraced also a seminary for the training of young priests. It was here that Monsieur Drach conducted his classes in Hebrew. Before Friday arrived, Jacob had taken Felkel into his confidence, meticulously making it clear that he was bound on a voyage of exploration only and that he would probably return in a few days, disillusioned, to throw himself utterly into material considerations and the search for employment.

"For," he confessed to his brother, "I find, Felkel mine, that as greatly as I abhor increasing the misery of our father, I cannot in honesty continue the rabbinical studies. In that, now four of his sons have disappointed him. There remain only David and Henoch to fulfill what he dreamed for all of us; and perhaps our young half brother Isaac. I despair at the thought of dealing him this blow. As for the possibility of dealing a further one by becoming a Christian, it seems unthinkable."

Felkel had nodded sympathetically; but inwardly had felt a long deferred hope take wings. . . .

Cold, silence, and darkness. Was there nothing in the world but these? Jacob looked up from the book he had been trying to read by the dim light which filtered down from a small window in the roof. His eyes met the narrow, whitewashed walls of a cell—here, a small hard bed; there, a stand and a straight chair; above the bed, a crucifix. That was all. From afar off came the toning of a muted, melancholy bell. Then silence again, silence as Jacob had never experienced before.

In utter misery he tossed the book across the bed. He could no longer bear this silence. It was oppressive, threatening, melodramatic. At any moment, it would surely be broken by a tragic shriek. For three days now, Jacob had waited for that shriek. But it never came. . . . Utter despair and loneliness. Hour after hour, poring over ancient, worn books—in Latin, in French, forbidden learning of the goyim. Hearing no human voice, except just before mealtimes in the long refectory where, with a lot of young men who seemed to know each other very well and to have much in common, he felt even more alone than in his narrow cell.

Drach. Yes, Drach had been very kind, but in their few interviews Jacob had been both drawn and repelled. The professor's hours at the seminary were crowded, and the talks in the stiff ecclesiastical parlor on the first floor had been necessarily brief. Their very setting lent to them an uncomfortable formality to which the volatile young Jacob was unaccustomed. He could not however forget Drach's kindness on that Friday—was it only three days ago?—when he had graciously introduced him to the superior, and to the others. They also had been kind and hospitable; but once they had shown him his cell, the library and the refectory, and the garden where he was privileged to take solitary walks, they had left him to himself. He had never realized before that goyim were such uncommunicative people. They said little, but worked and prayed much. Busy as bees, all day long; but distressingly untalkative. These, of course, were the religious in the long black soutanes which had always caused him repugnance.

Now he wondered if all Christian society was similar. Were the social gatherings of his brothers' friends as silent as the seminary groups? What an unpleasant thought! He smiled tenderly as he recalled the gatherings on the great Jewish feasts at his old home in Saverne. How everyone had talked and laughed at once—and eaten! How merry it had all been! But here during meals, no one spoke—except someone at the far end of the table who seemed to read aloud from a book. Jacob's seat was so far removed from his that he could hear nothing but a mumble.

Then, back to the solitude of his cell; or for a lonely walk in the garden, while the other young men hurried to strange preoccupations which seemed to keep them so happy—to chapel, to classes. If he had but one friend! Lazarus—where was Lazarus now? Busy at his law studies in Metz, hurrying to finish so that he might marry Esther. And his father? He wished with all his heart that a magic carpet would transport him on the instant to Save ne. There lay his Jewish roots. There, and there only, did he belong!

What was keeping him here, anyway? Why, at only a short distance lay Felkel's cosy rooms with a bed that Felkel had said was always to be his. He had but to walk out the door this minute and be with his brother in less than half an hour. He could leave a note for Monsieur Drach, who seemed to understand everything. And he need never return here, to this place as silent as the sepulcher, and as cold. Why was he troubling himself about religion, in any case? Many people lived quite happily without it, losing themselves in the pleasures of the world. Such pleasures were plentiful in Paris. He was but twenty-four. Why should he not forget religion and enjoy all that the world offered—freedom to work and to earn, to have friends and companionship, perhaps even a sweetheart whom he could marry and who would bear him children? The vision of Samson's peaceful home shot across his mind. Ah, but there religion entered in again! Could he never escape it?

The silence pressed in upon him relentlessly. Sighing, he languidly picked up the volume he had tossed across the bed. It was Lhomond, on the *History of Christian Doctrine*. That and a companion volume on the *History of Religion* had been left there for him by Drach. Although he had read them through, he found parts of them utterly incomprehensible, premised as they were on the essential keystone—faith. The

Eucharist . . . the miracles. And as he began to read again, his misery only increased. It seemed as though he were standing on the brink of a volcano, looking down into smoking depths and a vast, terrifying darkness. He could not turn back. There was no other way but to plunge. Into what? A bottomless pit? A raging, consuming fire, far below? But he must turn back. Now, before it was too late. After all, ages before this enigma ever existed, there had been the ancient faith of his fathers. . . . "I am the God of Abraham, and of Isaac. . . ." Desperately he again flung the volume from him. Then suddenly he found himself on his knees. Blind with tears, he broke into prayer.

"O Eternal God of my fathers, enlighten me, and lift the misery in which I wander, forlorn and alone. If this Christ is in truth Your Son and the Messiah, make it so known to me. But if this teaching is false, I beseech Thee, God of my fathers, save me from the abyss over which I tremble."

Only silence—only that all-encompassing silence of the seminary. He knelt there by the hard bed, his head buried in his hands, all the heart within him crying out to his God. Presently he lifted his head. And then, in that total silence, the answer was vouchsafed. From his mind, the clouds which for so long had shrouded it; from his heart, the fears which had chilled it, were lifted by a mighty force which left them naked and trembling. "For this was I born. For this came I into the world." In that silence, the ears of the spirit caught the words—and listened in ecstasy.

Then his eyes sought out the crucifix, hanging there above the bed. The late afternoon sun, moving westward, had sent a shaft of sunshine through the high window in the roof. It fell diagonally across the Figure of Him whose own had received

Him not. It illuminated the bent head, the outstretched arms. The rest of the room lay in shadow. And there on his knees, it was Jacob Libermann's voice which at last broke the silence with a joyous cry.

"Credo!"

What stupendous miracle is this—when God reaches down from heaven, and with His finger, touches a single soul! . . . It is Michelangelo's "Creation" as he dreamed it—but painted by the Divine Artist.

CHAPTER EIGHT

The Way

IT WAS CHRISTMAS EVE, and in that year of 1826 it fell on Sunday. Lying close to the Collège Stanislas, the little chapel of the Missionaries of France breathed in the still, holy silence which enfolded it. It was almost as though one could hear the beating of its heart.

Jacob was kneeling very quietly at his *prie-dieu* robed in white. He was happily conscious of being no longer alone. Ah, how long had he been alone! But now about him there knelt a handful of others to whom he felt linked by ties closer than any he had ever known; yes, even than to his father. He felt an instant's stabbing pain. ("Heavenly Father, guard him! And if it be Thy Will, grant to him this great grace, also!") And his mother, she whose death he had witnessed when he was but eleven? Somehow Jacob felt that she was near at this moment—and happy for him.

They had assured him that he was ready to be baptized, even though there was yet much to learn. It was only a few scant weeks since the gift of faith had been bestowed. Ever

163

since that day he had yearned constantly for baptism. How glad he was they had not postponed it!

These others about him, these comparative strangers to whom he now felt so oddly close—why should they give their concern to his most unimportant soul? It must be because of Jesus, who is the Way—and the Truth and the Life. While they awaited the arrival of the Abbé Augé, his friend Drach knelt at one side of him, and his beloved Felkel at the other. Of the five who were present, they three alone—they of God's Chosen People—best understood the long way he had come. His kindly godparents, who knelt at the right of Monsieur Drach, perhaps would never be able to understand the depth of his joy. They had always been Christians, the Baron François de Malet, and the Countess Marie d'Heuzé. Jacob felt a warm surge of affection for them.

As he thought of the Countess, whose numerous charities included a deep interest in converts, irrelevantly a memory from childhood stirred in his mind. That word "countess"? Oh, yes; the first time he had heard it—there in the shop of the widow Schaeffer in Saverne, where he had gone to buy the quills. A fabulous, feathered *Madame la Comtesse* had entered to purchase a Shakespeare. Jacob smiled involuntarily. At nine, how terrified he had been of "the goyim"! . . . He must not forget that he owed the widow Schaeffer one franc. If and when he could return to Saverne—he sighed—and if she should still be living, he would repay her.

Now from the rear of the chapel there came a slight sound —something scraping across the stone floor. Someone was moving a *prie-dieu*. Again, a sensation from childhood ran, fleet-footed, across his memory. That same sound when long ago he had fled in terror, into the dark church and stumbled against something, wondering what on earth it was. Then, he had been eleven. Now he was twenty-four, and about to be "born again." For at last he had come to understand Babette's phrase.

How he wished that Samson and Babette could be here. They had, of course, written—in great joy. But regretfully Samson had felt that he could not leave his practice just now —too many sick people. Why, it was only a few short weeks ago when, in all his egotism, he had sturdily resisted their Christianity, there in the cosy parlor at Strasbourg, his brother's home. But now he had found a new and deeper brotherhood with Samson, with Felkel and Samuel. How good was God!

Presently he felt Monsieur Drach's touch on his arm.

"The Abbé has arrived," he whispered.

With trembling knees Jacob arose. He had been well rehearsed in what he must do; he hoped he would forget nothing. The thin, gentle Abbé with the face of an ascetic, was standing there at the font vested in a white cope. Then the Baron and the Countess stepped to his side.

Now it was as though they were all moving through a dream. Beautifully and sonorously the Latin rolled on. Then came the exorcisms. Involuntarily his whole frame stiffened —and then lightened. To his amazement he felt as though he were being relieved of a heavy load that had long been a part of him, something he had carried all his life. The sensation left him faint. Then, as the cool water touched his brow, all reality vanished. He was caught up in a great globe of fire and light: he felt himself borne aloft among the spheres—

and for the first time, knew ecstasy. In that ecstasy there came to him the illumination of all his doubts; and a new and extraordinary feeling of strength.

"Francis Marie Paul," pronounced the Abbé Augé, "I baptize thee in the Name of the Father and of the Son and of the Holy Ghost."

And suddenly he knew what he must do. The soul of Jacob Libermann was on its knees, pledging then and there, in gratitude, dedication to the priesthood of Jesus Christ. "For after all, Eternal Father," he prayed beseechingly, "from the cradle I was dedicated to Your service. Now there can be no peace for me in anything but Your priesthood. From the depths of Your Infinite Mercy, accept me."

And when the seal of Christ was stamped upon his soul there in the chapel of the missionaries, on Christmas Eve of the year 1826, the eternal bridge leading from the Old to the New was once again traversed.

Early the next morning before the sun had risen, he partook of his first Holy Communion. "And I live, now not I; but Christ liveth in me." Veritably, he was born anew. And it seemed to him that he moved in the light and delight of the world's first dawn. . . .

He was very happy about his new Christian names: Francis, for his godfather, the Baron de Malet; Marie, for his godmother, the Countess d'Heuzé; Paul, for a double reason. It was not alone the name of his great friend, Drach; it was also the name of one who, like Jacob himself, had abandoned the synagogue for Christ, and who, proud of his Hebraic birth, had cried out to the world: "I am a Jew of Tarsus in Cilicia. . . ." "We preach Christ crucified." . . .

For in the few weeks at the college which had followed

upon that unforgettable afternoon in his silent cell, he had read much of Paul, and the Gospel of St. John, which now had taken precedence over his earlier passion, the Prophet Isaiah. Actually, the New Testament had been his constant companion, whether alone in the library, or moving from a lesson in catechism under the tutelage of Drach to a conference with his religious director.

How soon could he confide to Drach that he was determined to become a priest? Drach would at once point out the practical difficulties. No longer could be appeal to his father for funds—even though he might try to spare him for as long a time as possible from learning the truth. To the old Rabbi, this would be the bitterest blow of all. Let it come as gently as might be. It was only after much prayer that he finally approached Drach. Upon the young man's momentous announcement, the face of the converted rabbi had lifted with joy; only to fall again a moment later.

"But my dear Jacob—I mean, rather, Francis—how shall we manage? I could arrange to have you admitted to the seminary here at the college—there would be no difficulty about that. But what shall we do about your fees? Surely, you can no longer depend upon your father?"

The new convert sadly shook his head.

"Indeed, no. I am now wondering whether I should write to him and tell all: that I am a Christian, that I intend to become a priest. Or whether it's better—"

Drach was gazing reflectively out of the window.

"I'm thinking of your father," said he. "I remember what it was to be a rabbi. It's only a few months since he learned of the apostasy of two of your brothers, and before that he had the shock and disappointment of Samson. Better to wait a little. Some young men enter the seminary, and after a few months find that, after all, it is not for them. It is necessary to try it, to experiment."

"Ah," cried Francis eagerly, "you admit then that my entrance into the seminary might be managed?"

"I shall speak to the Abbé Augé, and also to your godmother, the Countess," promised Drach. "Her group of pious ladies interests itself in such cases." . . .

With grateful heart, Francis had gone to spend a few days with Felkel. There good tidings reached them: he was to be admitted at once to the seminary attached to the Collège Stanislas. Drach had sponsored him, and the good Abbé Augé, the Countess d'Heuzé and her group, had made the financial arrangements. The brothers Libermann were overjoyed.

The first winter weeks at the seminary passed rapidly as Francis threw himself with abandonment into the study of philosophy. While he had to work harder at his religious studies than those who had received their early instruction in Christian schools, he soon established himself as a good student. Apart from his classes at the seminary, he also attended some courses at the Sorbonne. But in his zeal to learn, he neglected sleep and recreation; and in the exalted spiritual state which possessed him, he lingered long at his devotions. What matter, if his old enemies, the headaches, returned fiercely from time to time? He would say nothing, happy to offer the suffering to his Lord. When they abated, he must work all the harder. For at twenty-four, there would be scant time left after ordination—should he attain to that—in which to serve. He must hasten to prepare well. And he had not even yet received the Sacrament of Confirmation. He must wait until Easter for that.

His mentors at the seminary were moved by an obviously flaming vocation. Seldom had they seen one burn at such white heat; and so it was not long before his spiritual director permitted him to receive the Blessed Sacrament three or four times a week—a privilege then reserved for the more devout seminarians. From this he always drew a renewed strength.

And yet—was it weakness that continued to postpone that letter to his father which must one day be written? There lay the only mar on his happiness. But Drach still counseled waiting. Devoutly he prayed the more for guidance; and as he had done when troubled during the lonely days in Metz, he wrote long letters to Samson. But it was Babette to whom he had written first, immediately following his admission to the seminary:

"What did you see, my dear Babette, with those other-worldly eyes of yours, on that day in Strasbourg when I bade you farewell? When you said I would become a priest, I thought you had taken leave of your senses. And now, behold, I have started on the very path you prophesied. That you held this thought of me when I was in a state of invincible ignorance and so far from grace, renews courage at those times when I become appalled at my unworthiness. Pray much for me, that all may be accomplished."

Needless to say, the house in Strasbourg had known great rejoicing when that letter was received. There was rejoicing also far away in America, when Samuel was apprised of the news. But the other brothers, Henoch and David, like their father remained for the time in ignorance. David was at home; and Henoch in the army, no one knew exactly where.

It was natural that the conversion of young Libermann should have become matter of discussion among his classmates at the seminary. Almost all of them were children of France and of sound Catholic background. That a Jew of Alsace, the son of a rabbi and himself trained for that life, should have suddenly embraced Catholicism, and as suddenly determined to enter the priesthood, was matter for both marvel and conjecture. Although for a time Francis had remained blissfully ignorant of it, in one way or another the word had been spread abroad. At length he was forced to recognize that while his fellow students were friendly, they yet seemed to regard him with a certain curiosity. Half humorously he told himself that their attitude indicated that he appeared to them as odd as the great awk. No matter. He was too busy, and too exalted, to be bothered by it. And so he remained until a certain day in early February.

On that afternoon, as he and other seminarians were leaving a class in history at the Sorbonne to return to Stanislas, young Bernard Tellier fell into step at his side. Bernard was a youth from the provinces, the son of a wealthy farmer. Nothing seemed to escape his lively, bright eyes in which there smoldered, even at that youthful age, the look of the exhorter.

"Tell me, Francis," he said, "how your father, the Rabbi of Saverne, received the news that you had become a Catholic and had begun to study for the priesthood? It must have been a terrible shock."

"Why, the truth is, Bernard, my father does not yet know."

"What? You have not told him?" Bernard's mouth was agape with astonishment.

"Not yet—under the counsel of my director."

"Ah! Your director then wonders whether your vocation is secure? That perhaps you may change your mind and leave us?"

"No—" hesitated Francis.

"I can see exactly what is troubling him!" exclaimed the zealous Bernard.

"Yes?" inquired Francis politely, wondering how soon he could rid himself of this unexpected inquisitor.

"Don't you see," pressed Bernard, "that your conversion and your vocation to the priesthood followed each other all too closely? Why, my dear Francis, these are matters which require years to determine! You should have been wise, and pondered these grave steps for a long time before embarking upon them. Think of your background. The son of a rabbi, and trained to be one yourself. Of course, you were too impulsive. Naturally, your spiritual director is concerned."

"But he is not concerned," explained Francis patiently, "that is, not about my conversion or my vocation."

"Then why does he not recommend that you inform your father immediately? At least, in all filial respect, that much is due the Rabbi of Saverne!"

Francis flushed. "There are reasons," he began.

"Nonsense," interrupted Bernard. "Come, confess that you acted hastily, perhaps on some youthful whim. First, true conversion to Catholicism could not possibly come so rapidly to one who knew practically nothing about it, who had given the dogmas so little study. But even granting that your conversion is real, and due entirely to divine grace, we face the further matter of your vocation to the priesthood. It may well be that you have a veritable vocation, but you should have taken longer to test it."

Bernard lifted his head and, as he strode along, extended his chest a trifle.

"After all, myself—I realized the seriousness of the step and therefore I gave myself two or three years in the world, doing the things of a young man of the world, to make certain. But you? Why, you are a mere babe, you have seen nothing of the world or its people! Furthermore, you have given scant consideration to your father who, after all, reared and supported you up to the present; and whose lifelong hopes you have, within a few months and without sufficient reflection, destroyed."

The young seminarian from Saverne was stricken dumb by the onslaught. He walked the rest of the way in silence, his heart aching miserably. That night as he knelt beside his bed in prayer, he could not restrain the tears.

"O Holy Spirit," he prayed, "beloved of my soul, enlighten me, guide me, console me. Tell me what I should do. . . . It would seem that Bernard is right. I have treated my father shamefully."

He did not sleep that night, for from the moment the candle was extinguished he was assailed by one of the worst headaches within his memory. By morning it had not abated and the seminarian, Francis Marie Paul Libermann, was missing from classes that day, unable to rise from his bed.

On the following day he sought out the Abbé Augé who had become his spiritual director.

"Patience, my son. I think Monsieur Drach is right. It is not yet time to send your father news that will only add to his already deep distress. What have you written him?"

"Nothing," said Francis miserably, "beyond a letter when I first arrived in Paris, telling him that I had called upon the

Grand Rabbi Deutz. I'm sure that my father remains under the impression that I am still with Felkel."

"It is as well, for the time, considering that he could not yet have recovered from the recent loss to the synagogue of two of his sons. Meantime, pray; and the proper course will at length be revealed."

Francis acquiesced with a feeling of great relief, for the advice coincided with his own innermost judgment. Then, as he was about to leave, the Abbé said gently:

"And don't pay too much attention to the Telliers, and such. They mean well, but all through life you will find people only too ready with their advice. In matters so personal as this, the only sure counsel is that which will come as you kneel at the foot of the Cross."

For Francis there followed two days of peace. But on the third, as he was leaving the recreation ground to attend his first afternoon lecture, young Tellier again joined him.

"Did you decide to write to your father, then?" he inquired.

"No; it is not yet time."

"But why? I cannot understand your delay. Believe me, Francis, you will one day rue it. Unless it be that you still feel uncertain of your vocation?"

Patiently Francis tried to explain.

"Those do not constitute good and sufficient reasons!" Bernard exclaimed.

Again Francis took refuge in silence. Within his soul he was praying for grace to overcome the irritation which, for all his efforts, persisted in rising.

"As your friend, and one who wishes you well, I must repeat that I think you acted too hastily," pressed Bernard.

Silence. Inner prayer. Then, just as they reached the lecture room, Francis turned to his companion with a smile of great sweetness.

"Thank you, Bernard."

That smile had been achieved with some difficulty; and later Francis almost regretted it. For rather than quieting Bernard, it seemed only to whet his zest for the assault. From then on, the young Jewish seminarian tried every device to elude him, but there were still countless occasions on which the two necessarily had to meet.

Frequently Bernard's zeal led him to mention the subject in the presence of others. Two of these, fellow students, one day found themselves alone following a particularly forceful exhortation by Bernard.

"What astounds me," said one, as he watched the figure of the victim disappear in the direction of the chapel, "is the patience of the Jew. Did you notice that he never replied a word to all of Tellier's impertinent proddings?"

"Yes; not only was he silent, but his manner gave no sign that he had taken offense. Had I been in his place, I think I might have let fly with one of my fists—may God forgive me!"

"And I, also. But I have noticed, my friend, that the son of the rabbi has already learned control better than have many of us. Also, that he possesses a great fund of inner serenity."

The other sighed. "I have noticed that, too. Why, I have begun to find that just being in the presence of Libermann gives me a feeling of peace. It does not matter whether we are discussing religion, sports, or politics. Somehow, I feel better for being with him. I don't understand it."

"Nor I. And yet, sometimes when I watch him at prayer," said the other reflectively, "I begin to think I understand."

Meantime, Francis was kneeling before the altar of Our Lady.

"My Lady Mother," he was praying, "you whose soul was possessed of all patience, help me!" . . .

Soon thereafter he began to realize that Bernard was utilizing the topic as a peg upon which to hang his moral disquisitions to the other seminarians. One day when he was returning from a solitary walk, Bernard's unmistakable accents came to him through an open window. A group had gathered in a corridor of the building as they waited for classes to resume. Just as Francis passed beneath the window, he heard what must have been the conclusion of a peroration by Bernard.

"After all, the conversion of a Jew should be well tested." Francis paused, involuntarily. "By its very nature, it is suspect. It is not a matter of a few months only; for all the world wonders, and has a right to wonder, how one of that race could be sincere in his adoption of Christianity."

As the words sank into his consciousness together with the realization that Bernard could have been talking about none other than himself, he felt a chill run through him. So that was it. That was the explanation. Bernard could not forgive him for being a Jew. Vividly there flashed across his mind words that had startled him long ago when as a little boy he had gone with his brothers to the harvest festival at Beaumont. "Sons of Jewish dogs, sons of Jewish dogs." In other words, outcasts. . . .

Later that day, when classes were over, he stole into the chapel. It was the quiet time, the hour of dusk, and he found his Lord alone there in the tabernacle, with only a dim light burning. As always at such moments the frightening dream of his childhood recurred—the small boat, the angry sea, the great light. . . .

"And all the time You *were* coming to save me, my Jesus; only then I did not know. I was a Jew. I am still a Jew. And You, too, were born a Jew, my Jesus. You, too, knew loneliness. An outcast, they tortured You, and nailed You to a cross."

And then, there in the quiet of the chapel, a great peace enfolded him; and he knew such sweetness as he had never before experienced. . . .

But although the frequent contretemps with Bernard had won Francis new friends among the more spiritual of the seminarians, he yet experienced many lonely and even agonizing moments—moments at night when he felt his father's avenging presence to be actually in the room with him, when he could almost see the anger and sorrow flashing from those dark eyes, deep-set in the noble and sharply defined face. Such mental visions almost always preceded a violent headache.

One night when he was suffering from a particularly severe attack and sleep was impossible, he arose from his bed, thinking that perhaps the cool night air might bring relief. The window was already slightly opened; but now he raised the sash higher and leaned out. It was late February and above him the stars and constellations burned with particular brilliance in the dark velvet of the sky. What was that St. James said about the Father of Lights? . . . "Every best gift, and every perfect gift, is from above, coming down from the Father of lights, with whom there is no change, nor shadow of alteration." How beautiful was the Christian literature! The lights above him shone in adoration of that Father, thought

Francis, and if only man could give testimony to his adoration as adorably as did these! Think of stars, of trees, of flowers—each His creation. Their just *being* shed beauty everywhere. But the beauty of man, His creature, dearer to Him than all else, was so often obliterated, overlaid with the ugliness of sin. . . . In whose eyes, besides those of God and his own, would he, Jacob Libermann, Francis Libermann, appear as a great sinner? But surely, in those of the good father far away in Saverne. . . .

Sighing, he closed the window softly and, with head still throbbing, turned toward his bed. But before he had taken two steps he was seized with an unaccountable dizziness, and was forced to grasp the back of a chair to keep from falling. Trembling there in the dark, struggling to remain upright, he suddenly felt a great fear. It was as though his body were being wracked by demons. His limbs vibrated violently, and the wooden chair under his shaking grip began to dance eccentrically. Terror enfolded him. For immediately he had recognized the seizure as something strange and powerful, something almost like a doom. After long moments it passed as suddenly as it had come, and he was able, with gasping breath and great weakness, to totter to his bed. Lying there in the quiet and the dark, gradually his breathing became easier and he was able to pray. "Merciful Father, thank You for permitting it—whatever it was—to pass." . . .

At length dawned the Easter Sunday of 1827, when Francis Marie Paul Libermann, with a group of other new converts, was confirmed in the faith by Archbishop de Quélen, of Paris. Now indeed, did the novice feel fortified with the strength of a lion.

In those days of the young spring the seminarians began to

look forward to the ceremony of the tonsure which would be held early in June. Those of the candidates who had proved themselves worthy would bow their heads to receive the sign which in that era identified all who had been accepted as aspirants for Holy Orders. Among others, his name had been solemnly read aloud in chapel, causing his heart to beat fast with joy. So much of the journey toward his cherished desire had been accomplished; not a great deal, to be sure—but so much.

But now he wished passionately that he could throw off the attacks of weakness which had been frequent ever since the night of the strange seizure. He began to watch for the dizziness—and to wonder. His step was perforce less rapid; and frequently when he should have been hastening from one lecture to another, he had to stop and grasp at something for support. His zeal for study was undiminished, but he found that he could not cover as much ground as formerly. If he pushed himself toward what had been his average goal, the next morning the effort was paid for, either with a throbbing head or an excess of weakness. He began to understand that he must, for the time at least, go more slowly.

He wrote a long letter to Samson, telling him of the seizure and his present condition, and asking for medical advice. Samson's reply was comforting, ascribing the symptoms to a heightened nervousness due to the drastic change in his life, but uttering a strong caution against overwork. Francis heeded it; and to his great happiness, on the ninth of June in the year 1827, the son of the Rabbi of Saverne received the humble Christian tonsure.

And now that summer had come to Paris, and she wore a lovely green gown against a background of silver river and blue sky, Francis began to feel a renewal of strength. He was able to study more, and met the examinations preceding the summer holiday serenely and successfully. Release from classes came in August; and he had been looking forward to spending as much time as possible with Felkel—and also to discussing at leisure with Drach a problem which had long been troubling him.

When the concluding lecture of the term had been delivered, he sought out a bench in a quiet corner of the garden where he attempted to draw up a plan for the vacation weeks. So much time for devotions, so much for prayer, so much for reading. Then Felkel; he must see him and they must make plans. But first of all he must call upon Drach and launch his problem. Sitting there in the leafy coolness of the garden, he again revolved it in his mind.

There was no avoiding the fact that all the seminarians at Stanislas were destined, if succeeding to ordination, to become missionary priests. For so the Archbishop had declared: that it was to be a training school exclusively for the missions. Francis had been a seminarian for some weeks before he had learned this. When the information had been vouchsafed, he had realized that he must take long counsel with himself, and in prayer, to try to determine whether his priestly vocation lay in that direction. And now he was certain that while he yearned with even greater ardor for the priesthood, he felt no call to the work of the missions. This, in all honesty, must be revealed to Drach. It was unthinkable that he should remain at Stanislas and be at the same time dishonest in his heart with his Archbishop—and with those whose charity was keeping him here. So the first portion of his holiday would be spent in resolving that important question. Then, too, there was the ever-present problem of his father. The last thing that Bernard, who had gone home on a visit to his parents, had said, was:

"Surely, Francis, now you will have time to write that necessary letter to your father."

His reflections in the garden were more disturbing than restful, and led to a wretched night followed by the inevitable headache. As he lay battling it, he tried to recall when it was that this old enemy had first attacked him. Ah, yes; it was immediately after his schoolmaster Mendelbaum had flung him against the wall. He had been nine years old. He recalled what an effort it had cost him not to cry. . . .

On the following morning, before he had reached Drach's door there had been at least two attacks of dizziness. And they reminded him of another thing he must discuss with his friend.

"But Francis, I think you are making too much of the missionary aspect. While it is true that the Archbishop has dedicated the seminary at Stanislas to training men for the missions, it is not a hard and fast rule that every seminarian should feel bound to such a vocation."

"Nevertheless, I must be open with him about it—more especially as I am a 'charity student.' Would you—would you mind terribly asking the Archbishop what he thinks I should do?"

"Not in the least. I expect to see him tomorrow; and I'm certain that he will advise that you remain where you are."

"I'm most grateful," said Francis. "And there's one other thing," he began hesitantly.

"Yes?"

"It's—it's about my health." He looked down shamefacedly. How humiliating it was to have to bring up this subject! Drach had been so kind. To trouble him with a further problem was obnoxious. Yet the candor and simplicity of Francis' soul forced it.

His friend listened with sympathy. "It's quite natural, considering all things," he said, "and it's probably nothing that cannot be cured by a little rest. If you are not better when classes resume, I shall advise that the rule of early rising be somewhat mitigated for you until the disorder has vanished."

The following afternoon Drach sought him out at the seminary.

"What do you think?" he cried, his face wreathed in smiles. "I was wrong after all, and you were right. The Archbishop was glad to be informed. Best of all, in the fall he is transferring you to the great seminary of Saint-Sulpice, and with a complete scholarship—all expenses paid!"

Francis could scarcely believe his good fortune. To study at Saint-Sulpice was the greatest privilege a seminarian could hope for. Its professors, men of renowned scholarship and virtue, were famous. And to be sent there, free from all anxiety about expense, was indeed the most generous gift his heavenly Father could have bestowed. His eyes were moist as the thanks flowed out, almost incoherently. And the moment Drach had left, he hastened to the chapel and prostrated himself for more than an hour in sheer thanksgiving. Then followed another hour of earnest prayer for his beloved father in Saverne. Drach had again counseled waiting.

When the summer had passed and the day arrived to bid farewell to his spiritual director, the Abbé Augé, Francis felt a pang of the heart. From the beginning, there had been a

Abbé always seemed to know exactly what he was thinking. And so it was on this morning when the young seminarian knocked at his door. The priest looked up from his breviary and, before Francis had time to utter a word, cried gaily:

"What! A pang in the heart, when you are off on such a great adventure? When you have become the petted protégé of the Archbishop of Paris himself? For shame, Francis Marie Paul Libermann—otherwise known as young Jacob!"

Ah, it was worth this sally, thought the Abbé, regarding his charge affectionately—just to see that smile break over the thin, sensitive face. What a smile it was, to be sure!

Eagerly Francis poured forth his gratitude, his assurances that he would visit him as frequently as was permitted. And finally he ended:

"If you would, but once more, give me your blessing, *Monsieur l'Abbé!*"

But after Francis had risen from his knees, it was the older man's final comment which evoked not only a smile but laughter.

"At Saint-Sulpice," he said gravely, "you will sorely miss your companion, Bernard Tellier. Try not to grieve too deeply."

"I shall try, *Monsieur l'Abbé*. Something tells me that I shall be able to pray for him there, much better than I can here!"

"Au revoir, *Archbishop* Libermann!"

"From all such misfortune, may the Lord deliver me!" laughed Francis as he took his leave.

It was a clear October day of the year 1827 when Monsieur Drach conducted him into the presence of Father Garnier, the venerable Superior of Saint-Sulpice. The heart of Francis misgave him a little as the priest, whose face bore every sign of intellect and ability, greeted him with a cool and aloof dignity. If the young man could have done so, he would have stopped Drach immediately from mentioning the matter of his health—but it was too late. His kind friend was already launched upon an explanation that the young seminarian's present physical condition demanded, for the time at least, that he be released from the customary early rising hour.

"In that case," announced the Superior, "he should not come here."

At that moment Francis wished that the ground would open and swallow him. Miserably, he looked at Drach. That one, rather than being nonplused, was continuing imperturbably:

"Young Libermann, while not yet fluent in Latin, nevertheless possesses a profound scholarship in Hebrew."

"The classes are conducted in Latin," pronounced Garnier drily.

There followed a pregnant silence. Francis felt sick and helpless. Obviously, this man did not want him—perhaps even despised him, for his weak Latin and his weaker health. Did he despise him also just for being a Jew? he wondered. He had better withdraw at once from Saint-Sulpice. But if so, what on earth would he do? ("Mother Mary, Mother mine, pray for me!") Although he did not know it, Father Garnier had meantime been carefully appraising the new applicant. Suddenly Francis was amazed to hear the Superior speaking again in a much gentler tone. Why, he was actually assuring Drach that he would be accepted in the seminary with the special privilege of rising later than the others!

In the new, wonderful days that followed, the seminarian

quickly learned that the Superior of Saint-Sulpice, for all his forbidding manner, was actually the kindest and most understanding of men. All the seminarians took pride in the fact that he had once been a pioneer priest in America, having gone out from France to help in the development of the young Church there. For a short time only did the new student find it necessary to utilize the privilege of late rising. Soon, and with no ill effects, he was actually rising not with the others at five o'clock but an hour earlier. The surcease in August had helped greatly. Now he was up every day at four, grateful for the privilege of serving the celebrant of the first Mass. This wonderful thing, the Mass! Much of its beauty was drawn from the Psalms which as a child, under his father's tutelage, he had learned to love. But now they had taken on a new significance for him as daily he participated in the great sacrifice and watched it move rhythmically toward its tremendous climax.

From his first day at Saint-Sulpice he had felt inspired. Part of the ancient rambling structure had stood there in quiet retirement on the Left Bank of the Seine ever since Paris was in her sixteen-hundreds. The very trees along the winding walks seemed to breathe out the perfume of sanctity. "Did you know," they whispered to him, "that real saints have walked beneath us? Saints and martyrs; for at least fifty bishops who were trained here died nobly for their faith during the Terror, when the streets of Paris ran red." The tradition of holiness and sacrifice touched the soul of Francis in its innermost recesses. Sometimes at the altar rail he felt the presence of those who had knelt there in the past, then eager young men like himself, but now long since dead, and who in great love had gone forth to expend their lives and unstinting labor solely in His service. They seemed to be whispering to him:

"Courage, young brother. You have only to ask, and He will help." . . .

As was customary with newcomers, an older student had been immediately appointed his "good angel," to advise him on rules and conduct in the seminary. Francis found his mentor, Georges, full of charity and understanding. Among his more mature guides and teachers there ranged an extraordinary strain of intellectual brilliance. A great many of them were members of the French nobility. His confessor, Father Faillon, the most spiritual of men, was at the same time a renowned scientist. One of the seminary's directors was the famous Father Mollevaut, simple and kindly, but despite his retirement from the world known throughout Europe as one of the greatest Greek scholars of his time. These and others of eminent scholarship soon recognized an intellect in the seminarian Libermann, and began to understand the quality of the finely grained spiritual nature they held in their hands for molding.

Francis, ever mindful of that first chill reception he had received at the hands of the Superior, went at his study of Latin with a will. He would not be a deterrent to others who were advanced beyond him. Continually he thanked God for having given him the good professor, Titescher, in Metz. But for that one's generosity he would not have had even a smattering of Latin, and might indeed have been denied entrance here. The "learning of the goyim"—he smiled over his Horace as he recalled the agonies of conscience with which he had embarked upon it. A few weeks of arduous work did wonders, and soon he found to his surprise that he could write well in Latin, and had little difficulty in reading the works of the Fathers.

His one stumbling block, when called upon to read aloud and translate in class, lay in the mystical theology of St. Bernard, with which, indeed, many a student more advanced than he had difficulty. St. Bernard—here again was the occasion for a quiet smile as the recollection of Bernard Tellier, whom he had left behind at Stanislas, crossed his mind. He wondered if there were something in the name—if "Bernard," in one form or another, were not actually one of the small crosses his Lord expected him to bear. But he never missed a day in praying for his erstwhile monitor. Between the seminary's daily community devotions, his classes and his studies, he could always manage an hour alone before the Blessed Sacrament.

Very soon he had become fascinated by the study of theology, his mind quick to absorb the fine points of dogma. Perhaps the long years he had spent interpreting the ancient Hebrew literature, insofar as they had developed a power to grasp subtleties, had not been lost after all. Making rapid strides in theology, he was also far and away the ablest Hebrew student in the seminary. All of which tremendously pleased his friend Drach.

Between them they had decided that the time to write his father would be at Christmas, when a year would have passed since his baptism. By that time he would have been for three months an accepted student at the great Catholic seminary. All this would convince the Rabbi that he had not acted upon a mere whim, that he was well started upon the new path and intended to follow it to the end.

Francis had already begun to compose the letter in his

mind. It would be full of tenderness, and in it he would employ all his powers to lay open the beauties of the Christian faith. As he thought about what he would write, he became more and more eager for the advent of Christmas.

One day, about the middle of December when the seminarians were gathered outdoors at their recreation hour, Francis stood with a group of three or four watching the progress of a lively game of ball. This was always a happy hour, not only set aside for relaxation and exercise, but also for the distribution of mail—the time when letters from home were received. The students themselves distributed the mail, and on this particular day it fell to the lot of young Georges, his "good angel," to approach him with a letter. As he drew near, he held it aloft and signaled gaily to his charge.

From Samson or Babette, thought Francis as he ran forward smilingly to meet the courier. For the truth was, he had apprised no one else in the family of his whereabouts, save Felkel who was sworn to secrecy until after their father should have been notified. As he took the missive and glanced at it, Georges was amazed to see his face turn an ashy white and the hand, which but a moment before had stretched forth so eagerly, tremble unsteadily.

"Thank you," said Francis uncertainly, as he turned away.

Apprehensively Georges gazed after him as he walked slowly to a far corner of the field. There, at some distance from the others, Francis unsealed the envelope. There had been no mistaking the handwriting. It was from his father.

Minutes passed as he stood there, turning page after page of the beloved one's writing, the tears openly streaming down his face. It was an enraged, incoherent indictment, violent and abusive. But every now and then it was interspersed quixotically with terms of endearment, as the old man implored his best-beloved son to renounce the apostasy which had entrapped him, and pleaded with him to return to Saverne and the synagogue. He was particularly bitter that his Jacob had not informed him of this step toward perdition. He charged him with being an ingrate, a traitor, a liar, and a coward.

"But," he wrote, "you see that you cannot deceive your father; for I have ways of learning what my sons are doing, even though they be at a distance. Be warned. If you do not heed this letter, I shall take more drastic steps to force your return. . . . It was bitter sorrow when three of your brothers committed this crime. But that you, upon whom all my hopes were founded, should have turned traitor is the heaviest affliction of all that the Almighty has seen fit to send your old father. Return, return, Jacob mine, to your home and my arms; to the arms of the synagogue where you belong.—Else will your father's curse forever hang heavy upon you."

Shaken by sobs, the young man cried aloud brokenly:

"But I am a Christian! I am a Christian!"

Only then was he conscious that his "good angel" had followed him. Georges came up and put an arm across the trembling shoulders.

"There," he said. "There, Francis. Nothing is so bad as all that. For the good God is ever at our side. What is it, my friend? Your father has found out?"

"Yes; and only a week or so more, and I would have written him myself. . . . I was only waiting for three months at Saint-Sulpice to pass . . . and now—"

Utterly broken, Francis sank to the ground and buried his head in his hands. His heart bled from a thousand wounds.

Georges sat down quietly beside him. After a time, he suggested softly:

"Perhaps you would like to see Monsieur Drach?"

"Yes, oh yes," cried Francis. "And Felkel! Felkel will understand."

And so, while Georges went off to consult Father Faillon who had come to know the soul of Francis in the confessional, and to seek his aid in sending messages to Drach and Felkel, Francis sat there as though held in a trance. Yes. Drach would understand. Drach who himself had once been a rabbi. He would advise him how to reply to his father. . . . But it was Felkel who would best understand, Felkel who had grown up with him in the old house next to the synagogue.

Drach was horrified, not that the Rabbi had found out—he had half expected that and had taken a long chance in his advice because it had seemed the better way—but horrified at the rage of the letter. He did his best, as did Felkel, to comfort the inconsolable Francis, assailed once more with a series of frightful headaches. When at length the young seminarian was able to see the paper on which he wrote, he penned a long and tender letter to the Rabbi, repeating his devotion and his lifelong gratitude—but asserting his deep Christian faith. He implored his beloved father also to turn to it—and to follow his four sons into the Church.

He waited long for a reply. It never came. At length David wrote. Their father was ill. He, David, had also been forced to disappoint him. He had tried his best, there at home, to complete his training for the rabbinical career; but the more he had studied, the less it had held him, until now he had reached a stage of total unbelief. So now, of the six sons whom the Rabbi had destined to follow him, there remained only

Henoch; and it was almost certain that he would never adopt such a career, having until now remained in the army. At the moment, they did not even know his whereabouts. . . . Of course, there was the young half brother Isaac, who was now eleven. He was very devout in his religion and an excellent Hebrew scholar. He reminded them all very much of Jacob when he had been of the same age. . . . Perhaps Isaac, the last, would in the end be the only Rabbi Libermann. In any case, their old father, broken in health, would never live to see it.

The letter only redoubled his sorrow. He took his grief to the foot of the Cross. And there finding solace, he prayed for his father's peace; and pleaded for the grace of conversion for his brothers, David and Henoch—and also for their sister, Esther, and her betrothed, his friend Lazarus.

Finally there came a letter from Esther. Sorrowfully, Francis knew, even before he opened it, the tidings it carried. Their father was dead. . . .

It was many weeks before his companions again saw the attractive smile flash across the face of the Jewish seminarian. What they did see was an increased devotion and piety; and what they noticed most was an exquisite charity. Thus it fell out that one of the directors, Father des Loges, whose task it was to draw up the weekly list of seminarians who each in turn would spend a period of adoration before the Blessed Sacrament, always contrived to assign Francis to the same hour as himself. Only he knew why. It was his own secret that he had but to watch Francis in the presence of his Lord, to feel his own devotion renewed and restored. . . .

After the storms of 1827, the year 1828, his second at Saint-Sulpice, passed calmly for the seminarian. Francis felt he had "come into port." The seminary, his companions and teachers were no longer strange to him. He had made many friends. Nor were the studies as difficult. Moreover, he had learned to take better care of his health. The headaches were fewer, and the once alarming dizziness had almost vanished. He was forced to recognize that in some odd way the death of his adored father had brought a certain relief. It was wonderful now to be able to write without restraint to those of his family who remained in Saverne; to Lazarus who was nearing the end of his law studies in Metz, and would soon be married to Esther. Through those at home, he was endeavoring now to ascertain the whereabouts of Henoch, so that he might write him of the happiness he had found in Christianity. With Samson and Babette he exchanged weekly letters, and on almost every visiting day, Felkel came to see him at Saint-Sulpice.

Moving serenely through the seminary routine, he began to cherish its silences. He recalled how the silence of his cell at Stanislas, during those first suffering days when he was grasping at a faith, had oppressed and almost strangled him. Now, he wooed the silences, for he had learned that they brought him that much closer to God.

Steadily he worked toward his next objective, to be achieved just before Christmas, when he would receive minor orders. That much toward the goal of priesthood would have been accomplished. Following that, there would remain the great goal of the subdeaconship, the first of the three major orders, when he would bind himself forever to the priesthood. It would be only a matter of little more than a year from now.

When on December 20th he entered the chapel to receive minor orders from the same hands that had confirmed him, Archbishop de Quélen looked upon him with satisfaction.

This was the young man who, at Stanislas, had been scrupulously honest; had sent him word that he was not a candidate for the missions. His protégé had done well at Saint-Sulpice, and the Archbishop of Paris rejoiced. It seemed likely that one day he would be a credit to the priesthood of France.

Dawned the winter of 1829. It was particularly cold and bitter, and as the sharp winds from the Seine blew across Saint-Sulpice, they found crevices in the old building and whistled briskly through the long corridors. The seminarians and the professors shivered at their tasks and drew their cloaks closer about them. That of Francis, which he had bought cheaply upon his arrival in Paris—the one he had given to the old soldier in Strasbourg had been of much better material—was already worn threadbare. He suffered intensely from the cold, but now, deeply conscious of the privilege and dignity of minor orders, plunged himself into increased devotions and study. It was not long before he began to pay for this.

At first, he treated the recurring dizziness as one would treat a petulant child—favoring it slightly but also submitting it to the discipline of being ignored. To his distress, he soon learned that this treatment was ineffectual. The headaches only increased; the dizziness frequently caught him at embarrassing moments. It was humiliating, for instance, to have to clutch at a doorpost just when the Superior was passing and about to give him a kindly word.

Again, he wrote to Samson, in his fear lest he should lose ground in his preparation for the subdeaconship. Nothing must delay that.

Off in Strasbourg some days later, Dr. Libermann sat reading the letter and tapping his teeth reflectively with a pencil.

"How is he?" asked Babette, looking up from her sewing.
"Not well. I'm anxious."

He read aloud a paragraph from the letter. "I think that mental application has fatigued me. As soon as I try to work a little, I feel an excessive pressure, as if my forehead and temples were girt with an iron band."

"Oh, Samson; we must pray the rosary for him tonight. Nothing must happen to defer his ordination." . . .

While on his part, in Paris, Francis read over several times Samson's reply:

"You must take more rest. You must recall, Jacob mine, that you have ever had a more sensitive nervous structure than the rest of us. I remember being struck by this when you were a very little boy, and I was only in my early teens. Somehow I knew that you suffered more than the other brothers from the normal emergencies which always occur in family life. I recall, too, how ill you were as an infant, and how anxious were our parents. All this points to the necessity of guarding your health, particularly now when you are approaching the tremendous event which we all await with what feelings of joy you cannot imagine. The momentous changes which have occurred during the past two years have been a strain. You positively must take more rest."

Accordingly, as the months passed, Francis reluctantly gave up many of the practices of devotion which had become precious to him, in order to lie, a victim in his bare cell, his eyes fixed imploringly upon the crucifix. Yet the forced hours of rest, the dangerous slackening in his studies, did not seem to help. By early spring he was utterly discouraged, and even tried manfully to face the fact that he might, in all honesty, be forced to quit Saint-Sulpice. The Archbishop should not be expected to support an invalid seminarian unable to keep abreast of the schedule. Then fortuitously in April, there arrived from Stanislas for a few days' visit, his old friend, the Abbé Augé. Francis, lying on his bed in utter dejection, heard the quick footsteps approach his door.

"*Entrez.*"

"Ah, my dear Francis, I bring you warm greetings from your friend, Bernard!" began the Abbé, with a twinkle. But in an instant: "Why, what's the matter?"

Haltingly, Francis told him. The appalling headaches, the attacks of dizziness, the lost time from studies—his fears about the subdeaconship.

"We'll cure that," declared the undaunted Abbé. "I will take you back with me to Stanislas for a time, where your duties will be light, with plenty of enforced rest; and you will soon be well again."

And so it was arranged with the Superior of Saint-Sulpice. Under his friend's kindly care the young seminarian began to improve and by midsummer was entirely well again. Happily he rejoined his companions at Saint-Sulpice for the opening of the fall term, where immediately all were plunged into their preparations for ordination. It was to take place in Advent, during the ember days just before Christmas. Francis, his courage restored, the eyes of his soul fixed upon the priesthood, renewed his theological studies with vigor, and doubled his devotions.

Frequently now, following a class, some of his companions would seek him out at the recreation hour to ask his explanation of this or that theological point. Very simply he would give his reply, but soon, as the discussion waxed, a light would seem to illuminate him from within. With face aglow, he would voice profoundly spiritual thoughts, clothing them in a rare beauty. Gradually a group would gather about him. Once, immediately following such a discourse and when all were hastening back to the lecture rooms, the Superior, who happened to pass along a corridor, was startled to overhear one seminarian say enthusiastically to another:

"You should have been there! You should hear how the young Jew can speak of *le Bon Dieu!*"

The Superior smiled to himself. He, too, was satisfied with the progress of "the young Jew." His judgment, after all, had been right, although he had doubted it on that October morning two years ago when Drach had presented one who had seemed an unlikely aspirant for the priesthood—a youth deficient in Latin and incapable of early rising! . . .

The eight days of retreat, of intensive meditation and prayer, which preceded ordination had been accomplished. Never had Francis felt himself so deeply attuned to the call of his Master. Apart from this, it was Advent, a time of year he particularly loved, when all the world seemed to hang breathless waiting for the moment when the Infant King would be born. And all through these days, especially tender were his prayers to the young Mother. The ceremony of the subdeaconship, when he would pledge himself forever to the service of the King, was set for the following day. But in his joyful anticipation he must not forget others less fortunate than he.

There was, for instance, young Jarrier, who lay ill in the infirmary. He would spend his recreation hour with him, following the brisk five-minute walk which Samson had made him promise he would take daily. Poor Jarrier. Francis knew better than most how discouraging it was to lie suffering upon a bed, wondering whether one would ever be able to resume a normal life. He had in his pocket for the patient his most prized medal of Our Lady—one that had been given him by the Abbé Augé.

When he returned from his walk, the recreation hour was at its zenith. As he made his way through the lively groups, exchanging a smile and a word here and there, he heard steps running after him. Turning he saw one of the new seminarians hurrying toward him with a letter.

"I've been looking everywhere for you!" cried the youth.

Smiling his thanks, Francis took the missive and paused to open it. Ah, it was from Henoch! For at last the family had heard from him only a month before, and Francis, upon learning his whereabouts, had written him happily of the wondrous thing that had befallen him. This would be Henoch's reply. He sought a near-by bench and sat down happily to read it.

The opening sentences were puzzling; they seemed cold and unfriendly—not at all like his dear Henoch. He read on. Then came the blast. "By your unforgivable apostasy I am convinced that you caused the death of our father. And I, for one, shall never forgive you."

Francis dropped the letter as though it had been a flaming brand. His breath came in short, stabbing gasps. His brother accused him of killing their father! . . . He did not know how long he sat there, oblivious of the laughter and talk about him, of those who passed and eyed him curiously. "Do not, I beg, seal your treachery by taking the final step toward the Catholic priesthood. Do not place this crowning insult upon the grave of our venerable father, he who was the Rabbi of Saverne."

Finally Francis rose unsteadily to his feet. For all his anguish, he must not neglect the visit to his sick friend, there in the infirmary. He moved forward falteringly.

Ah, yes; there it was—and to be expected. The preliminary throbbing at the temples, the dizziness. But surely he could reach the infirmary without grasping for a support. Only a few steps more. . . .

Then suddenly the earth heaved convulsively under his feet and he was thrown violently to the ground. He lay there, writhing in contortion, his limbs, his entire frame, torn mercilessly by a legion of devils.

Those near by had heard his anguished cry, and came running. They beheld their loved companion, who in truth had become their model in the spiritual life—the seminarian, Francis Marie Paul Libermann—cast to earth, writhing under the violent flogging of an unseen force. The pupils of the soft, intelligent eyes were almost invisible. And the poor mouth, known for its charming smile, was now contorted and almost obliterated by a froth of bloody foam. . . .

In pity and horror, they threw a cloak over him to hide his humiliation. Then, when the body was limp, they carried him to the infirmary and placed him on the bed next to that of the friend he had been going to visit.

It was epilepsy—the *grand mal*. And there at Saint-Sulpice on that December day of the year 1829, the eve of ordination, all knew that Francis Libermann had lost the priesthood—forever, as they thought. For was not the dread disease supposed to be incurable? And did not Holy Mother Church regard it as a total impediment to the priesthood?

CHAPTER NINE

The Cross

THE DOCTOR HAD just told him. It was very quiet in the infirmary now that he had gone—quiet and cold, for the fire in the little iron stove had gone out, and someone had forgotten to rebuild it. Indeed, thought Francis, with all the unusual stir of the ordinations to be held tomorrow, and as busy as they all were, this was not remarkable. The ordinations! He turned his head on the pillow lest young Jarrier, who lay in the bed next to his, should see the tears.

Jarrier was feigning sleep, but Francis knew he was awake and was lying there with closed eyes, not knowing how to comfort his companion. Poor Jarrier! It was hard for him. For of course he had heard everything the doctor had said, had followed intently his close questioning.

Dr. Lombard, who was the attending physician at Saint-Sulpice, had, in fact, been in and out of the infirmary twice that afternoon. The second time he had drawn his chair close to the prostrate young man and had closed his hand over the

one that lay listless and enervated upon the white counterpane.

"My friend," he had said, "I have been talking with those
who were there when you fell. There can be no doubt. It was
an epileptic seizure. But you must not lose heart. You must
remember all the great men who have suffered from this
malady—famous warriors and artists and saints—who yet
have lived to do great deeds, to lead noble lives."

"One—one cannot be cured?" asked Francis bravely.

The doctor pulled at his short, gray-flecked beard.

"Well, I would not say that," he began cautiously, "but—"

He broke off to look down with sympathy into the searching dark eyes.

"But it is a barrier to the priesthood, is it not, doctor?" The
words came softly, steadily.

The older man nodded his head, not trusting himself to
speak. . . .

Now that he had gone and it was so quiet in the infirmary,
Francis could pray. ("You called to me, my Lord, there in the
chapel of the missionaries, three years ago—'Come, follow
Me.' It must be that You have not found me worthy. That,
I understand only too well, my Jesus. Thy Holy Will be
done!") Then, with a sigh, he had dropped off into a deep
sleep.

He awakened from his dream with a start, to find the Abbé
Augé bending over him.

"My son—"

The Abbé was looking down into eyes still shrouded with
dream and dark with tragedy. The pale lips moved.

"My father's curse," whispered Francis.

"Ah, no!" exclaimed the Abbé, almost sharply. "You are too

good a Christian to believe that! It is only *le Bon Dieu* who
has the power to afflict, as well as to bless."

"Forgive me, *Monsieur l'Abbé.*" He passed his hand across
his brow, then turned toward his old friend with a characteristic smile which immediately banished the melancholy over-
shadowing the sensitive face. "It was only a dream." . . .

The Abbé had come to assist at the ordinations, and when
they had told him what had befallen, he had lost no time in
hastening to the infirmary. Now he sat for an hour or more
with the victim, soothing the bewildered soul with his gentle
words. His finely spun spirituality was both poetic and log-
ical, and when he had gone the heart of Francis beat again
with courage.

Thus it was that the New Year of 1830 found at least one
seminarian at Saint-Sulpice with plans altered involuntarily
and facing an enigmatical future. At first, when feeling better,
he had resumed his classes as usual, for, to his infinite relief,
nothing had been said about his leaving the seminary. He
assumed that the kindly Superior, who never acted hastily,
was waiting to see how things would go—was even hoping
like Francis himself that there would never be another seizure. ("But only, dear Lord, if You should so desire it.")

He had met his classmates again as naturally and as simply
as though nothing had happened. At times he could almost
believe that nothing had—were it not for the fact that he
tired more easily and had to put away his books earlier.
"Rest," the doctor had cautioned, "and more rest." It was easy
enough to say, but hard to accomplish if one were to keep
abreast of the studies.

Then, after some weeks, implacably the scourge struck
again. He had been mounting a stairway of the old building,

one worn into deep hollows by the feet of generations. As with two or three books under his arm he neared the last step, suddenly the alarm flashed—that blinding pain in the head—and he knew in an instant what was to befall. Instinctively he threw himself forward across the landing to avoid being hurled back upon the stairs, emitting a strangled cry. And there those who came running found him, writhing under the pronged lash of his enemy. . . .

As the months passed and the seizures continued at intervals, Dr. Lombard, ever watchful, noted that they varied in intensity—at times, severe; at others, slight.

Following the attacks, when Francis lay weak and helpless, not many of his classmates visited him, although the face of his "good angel" Georges was almost always the first he saw upon regaining consciousness. When he would reappear at the lectures, pale and wan, many seemed embarrassed if he approached them with a simple question. Pressed by Francis, Georges had told him why. He explained as gently as he could that his friend's appearance during a seizure disturbed anyone who might be near. His physical torments were so obvious that witnesses could not meet him afterward without being torn between the impulse to express their sympathy and the desire not to humiliate him by referring to the occasion. Francis himself, upon regaining consciousness, had no memory at all of what had occurred.

The soft dark eyes looked puzzled.

"But I would not be humiliated," he explained.

"I know," said Georges, "but they think you would. For it is known that victims of the malady usually wish to conceal it from everyone."

This talk enabled Francis better to understand why those

who had once been eager to discuss some point of theology, and who had followed his every word when he had discoursed upon *le Bon Dieu,* now studiously avoided him. He realized they feared to be unwilling witnesses of a seizure. It would be a very unpleasant task, he reflected, for those who in all charity would feel compelled to carry him to his bed. That was why, upon awakening from the deep sleep which invariably followed, the first thing he asked was the identity of those who had helped him. He could not rest until he had told them unrestrainedly of his gratitude.

But within himself he could not deny that he sorely missed the little admiring groups which had formerly gathered about him during the recreation hours. And this human weakness he counted a fault.

As the months passed and the seizures continued, upon orders of the Superior he was forced to drop first one class and then another—until finally he realized that he could scarcely any longer be considered a student. This was his gravest trial. But the free hours which were thus afforded he spent in the chapel. There, only two were present: his Lord and himself. The flickering sanctuary lamp played silently upon the suffering figure hanging on the cross. Kneeling there in the stillness he confessed his struggles and his defeats. Over and over again he repeated his humble *Fiat.*

"They deserted You too, my Jesus, in Your dark hour—and You were God. . . . When You fell beneath the load and Roman boots kicked You to Your feet, fastidious eyes also turned away from your shame—and You were God. . . . When soldiers wove the crown of thorns and crushed it upon Your head, that pain too could hardly be endured—and You were God. . . ."

Presently and surely, what had been a monologue there in the silence of the chapel became a dialogue whose surpassing sweetness was audible only to the soul of Francis Libermann.

One day in early June Dr. Lombard, looking thoughtful, knocked at the Superior's door.

"I've come about young Libermann," he said as he placed his bag on the floor and approached Father Garnier's desk. "I've just left him in the infirmary."

The Superior pushed aside a pile of correspondence and motioned him to a chair.

"I'm glad," he said, "for I've been wanting to talk with you. Is there any improvement?"

The doctor shook his head.

"I fear not. It is certainly epilepsy; both *grand* and *petit mal.*" He sighed. "Medical science has not progressed very far since the days of Hippocrates in treating this malady. The ancients viewed it as a curse of the gods. Hippocrates believed that when one is stricken in young manhood—at the age of Libermann—there is no chance of a cure."

It was Father Garnier's turn to sigh. "It's a great pity," he said, "for I had held the highest hopes of him. Seldom have I seen as true a vocation." He fell into a moment's silence. Then reflectively, he added, "It seems strange, my friend, that the good God should have seen fit both to call him and to repel him."

"Equally strange is the patient's attitude," commented the doctor. "That is really the great puzzle of the case."

"His attitude?"

"In all cases of epilepsy the reaction following a seizure is one of extreme depression. The patient suffers from a deep melancholy, a profound sense of shame, and frequently is tempted to suicide."

"And Libermann?"

"He is baffling. He defies all rules. I have seen him now at many such times. But rather than finding a patient gripped with melancholy, I find one who is completely serene—quite undisturbed emotionally. Instead of being absorbed in self-pity, as is usual, he is to the contrary only concerned about others and regretful of the trouble he may have caused them. Each time I enter the infirmary to be greeted by that extraordinary smile, I cannot believe—until I have examined him—that he has actually experienced a seizure. Yet of that there can be no doubt. . . . I tell you, *mon père*, that young man is either an angel or a saint!"

The few companions who visited Francis after an attack had begun to hold the same conviction. But it was a secret only between Francis and his Lord how great was his struggle, and how painful the uncertainty of his future, for he could not conceive of a life for himself which was not completely devoted to the service of God.

Monsieur Drach had visited him and as usual his practical mind had counseled against any hasty decision. Time would reveal the Will of God. Felkel, more deeply distressed than had he himself been the victim, came regularly now, bringing small gifts and trying unsuccessfully to hide the despair lurking in his eyes whenever he looked upon his brother.

As was his custom in extremities, Francis wrote frequently to Samson. "I do not know what will become of me, but I feel that it is not possible that God will abandon me." The loving replies of Samson and Babette were a source of solace. "How I wish I might come to you, my brother," wrote the doctor.

"But you are apparently in excellent hands, and all is being done for you that I could do. I would come in any case, but as you know our family is increasing and I am needed here by many—especially now that they have made me mayor of the little town of Illkirch. Meantime our prayers are with you constantly."

As for letters, the one which had come from Henoch, and which had been in his hand when he had first fallen there on the recreation ground, he had never answered. After all, what was there to say? In time, in God's good time, perhaps the scar it had burned upon his heart would heal.

Although restricted in attendance at lectures, he was left free to participate in the works of charity which were a part of the seminarians' routine. Among these he found his greatest satisfaction when assisting at the weekly disbursement of alms and clothing to the poor. On a day in late winter while penning a letter to Samson, he was notified that he had been assigned, together with Jarrier, to this privilege. Putting aside the letter, he hastened to the hall where the unfortunates were waiting. On this cold afternoon there was a larger number than usual. His heart beat with compassion as he stood with his companion at the long table laden with garments and food, and surveyed the pitiful ranks: old men in threadbare jackets, and old women shivering under thin shawls; young mothers with pinched faces, a baby in the arms and two or three little ones pulling at their skirts. Each face bore the mark of suffering; each, he longed to comfort. He sensed that these understood as did few others, the patient acceptance of God's Will. And he felt very humble in their presence.

Gradually the ranks moved forward to receive their alms, but due to the unusually large number the distribution went slowly. Presently some in the rear began to grow restless and pushed against those in front. All at once these, forced by the pressure, broke ranks and converged *en masse* upon the two dispensers.

"*Ciel!*" cried Jarrier. "We are submerged! Please tell them, my friend, that those who push will receive nothing."

Francis turned and looked at him in amazement.

"You mean—that we should actually impose a penance upon these poor unfortunates?"

Jarrier flushed.

"I'm sorry, Francis. For a moment I forgot why we are here."

From that time forward the poor knew there was one at Saint-Sulpice who loved them. Each week they watched hopefully for the young "abbé" with the gentle smile, and who looked so oddly like a Jew. . . .

It was about this time that he had news from Saverne. His little sister Esther and his friend Lazarus had been married. They wrote to tell him of their happiness, and how much they missed him. They knew nothing of his illness, for which Francis was thankful. Lazarus had splendid expectations as a young attorney in his own town, and there they would make their home, "very near the synagogue," he wrote, "which is what we both desire." . . . Francis sighed. He remembered how close Lazarus had been to his own spiritual quest, back in the far-off days of Metz. Why, he had been nearer to Christianity than had Francis himself! It was Lazarus who had actually directed him to Monsieur Drach. And now here he was more securely attached to the Old Law than ever. Dear Esther . . . in the long years at home, their father had made certain that she would never desert the synagogue. And from the start of the romance Francis had known that Lazarus would go wherever she led. But if he could only see them again—if he could but talk with them! He was certain he could convince them.

As he reflected on the pleasure of such a meeting, he began to wonder whether he and Lazarus could perchance ever recapture the lighthearted laughter of their student days. Again he sighed. What laughter indeed could there be at such a meeting of three who loved each other, if suddenly one of the three were flung to the ground and horribly distorted before their eyes? No, it would be best if he never saw them or Saverne again. . . . Now, of that once large and lively family, only four remained in the old house: David—who had written that he was chafing to get away to find employment near one of his brothers; and their stepmother, Sarah, with the two young ones, Isaac and little Sarah. If God would only call them all into the Church! But he, Francis, would certainly be a poor and unfit apostle amongst them just now.

When summer came to Saint-Sulpice, mounting the old stone steps with a dainty grace, Francis began to feel better. But in his mind he surveyed the record of his malady since December . . . and marveled at the Superior's patience. No hint had been cast, no word had been said, about his leaving the seminary. He knew then that the Superior held the same faith to which he himself clung—that he would eventually be healed.

A few miles from Saint-Sulpice and Paris, and off in the green countryside, lay the villa of the Solitude, an adjunct of the Paris seminary which rose on the picturesque hill of the little village of Issy. Here were trained the novices of the Society of Saint-Sulpice; here also came all the Paris seminarians for their advanced philosophical studies. In a sense, it was also a place of relaxation for the students of Saint-Sulpice, for it had been arranged that on one day of every week a group of them would journey to Issy for meditation and long walks in the country air. Francis loved the place. Here, far removed from the stir of the city and the activities of the great seminary, under the open sky and through the fields, through the whispering mysteries of the wooded walks, he felt closer to his Father in heaven. Here he could really listen as nowhere else to the song of his old companion, the wind.

In the year 1830 it so fell out that early on the morning of July 28th, Francis set out happily with a group of students for this retreat. After they had arrived and he had made his customary visit to the chapel, he emerged under the blue sky and was about to choose one of his favorite walks. It would be unlikely that anyone would wish to accompany him, he reflected. But to his surprise and pleasure, he was joined almost at once by the gentle-faced John Salier—one of the few who made a point of visiting him after the seizures. Groups of other seminarians stood about, some laughing and jesting, others talking seriously, and several with books under their arms. It was a perfect July day, replete with sunshine and bird song. Then suddenly the quiet air was shattered by a fearsome sound. Startled, all paused to listen. It was the tocsin of Paris, shrieking its alarm. Almost immediately it was followed by the loud booming of cannon.

As they waited uncertainly, the sound came nearer; the cannonading grew louder and more frequent. It had come, then, the civil war which many had foreseen and feared. Between the so-called reactionary trends of a restored monarchy and the liberal ideas which had sprung from the Revolution, the monarchy of Charles X had faltered and failed. The workers had taken over Paris and were fighting the government troops. Despite the king's expedition against Algiers, his victory which was to prove the prelude to the conquest of Algeria, the workers were more interested in unrestricted opportunities at home and more liberal suffrage—and were prepared to die for them.

As the cannonading grew louder, the seminarians ran excitedly hither and thither, wondering whether they should return to Paris . . . fearful of the fate which might be dealt there to the priestly household of Saint-Sulpice. For it was well known that the revolutionary movement was anticlerical. Some ran to the gates of the Solitude and scanned the road for refugees. These were not long in arriving, for now Francis could hear the rapid beat of hoofs coming down the country road.

Presently he saw a baker's cart draw up at the gates in a great cloud of dust. It was surrounded in an instant by an excited group, all crying out questions and talking at once. Above the din rose the news that the insurrectionists were manning the barricades and that the dead were strewn about the streets of Paris. The artillery was mowing down all within reach of the guns—innocent unfortunates who had been caught abroad, as well as the revolutionists. In sections held by the latter, sacrilege was being committed against the churches. The priests had fled. . . . Would the battle extend to Issy?

Salier, who had run forward with the others to hear the report, now looked around for Francis whom he had left standing immobile, his eyes strangely remote. To his surprise,

Libermann had vanished. Somewhat alarmed, he ran up and
down the winding paths which skirted the villa, searching for
the epileptic. At length he came upon him in an arbor, his
face bathed in tears.

"What is it?" cried Salier.

"My friend," murmured Francis, "at this moment no one is
thinking of God. In the hour when they most need Him, His
children have forgotten Him. Now, above all times, we should
pray and should go forth to succour the poor dying souls; and
to protect the houses of God, even to the death. Yet here we
run about in great confusion, with neither prayer nor action."

When the battle which lasted three days was done, the
seminarians returned to Paris to find to their joy that Saint-
Sulpice had been left unmolested. Charles X was in exile, and
had carried the white flag of the Bourbons with him; and for
the time, a political coalition ruled France. But under the disturbed conditions which continued for a long time to shake
the capital, the Superior and his staff knew many an anxious
hour. Those with whitened hair recalled only too well the
brutal anticlerical excesses of the Revolution; the intervening
two-score years were as but a day. Within their memories,
blood still ran crimson in the streets . . . and they prayed to
their brethren of Saint-Sulpice who had died as martyrs at
that time. It could happen again. . . .

Francis had survived the excitement—and indeed the entire summer—with no more than occasional slight seizures.
He was grateful to God that he was able to recognize more
and more the physical premonitions which preceded the attacks: the great mental weariness, the feeling of total enerva-
tion, the throbbing temples. When the danger signals began

to fly, he would retire quietly to his room and close the door, relieved that he could spare others the painful and revolting sight of himself. There, in praper before his crucifix, he would calmly await the event. He had come to recognize his malady as a precious means of acceptance of the Will of God, an opportunity of offering sacrifice to the Most High. In such a light, he could even think of it with actual affection. So now he began in his letters and in his speech to refer to it as his "dear malady."

But although upon the opening of the new term he was better, the Superior and the doctor would permit none but the lightest schedule of studies. Neither of them were unobservant of the wistful expression of which Francis himself was quite unconscious, but which would steal over his face as upon the sound of the bell, others hurried to classes and he was left standing alone. One day the Superior sent for him, Francis, hastening to the office, was overcome with fear that at last the word of exile was to be spoken. But Father Garnier, looking up with a smile, only said:

"It would be a good idea if you would mingle more with the others at recreation periods. Formerly, many found great help and inspiration in your little informal talks. You have an ability to lead others, to strengthen them, in this manner."

The thin, pale face broke into a smile of pleasure.

"Thank you, *mon père*. I shall try. But my dear malady—it is terrifying to others, and I do not wonder that more do not seek my company."

"That is true, my son," said the Superior gently, "but we are at the start of a new term. There are many newcomers who have not witnessed a seizure. It is particularly with the new men that I wish you to talk. Meantime, if it pleases God, your malady may leave you one day as suddenly as it came. Now it would be well to employ the time when others are attending lectures, in consideration of certain spiritual topics which you think would be helpful, so that when you discourse you will have a plan in mind."

The Infinite Goodness of God! The Superior had found a use for him—for one who had been so utterly useless.

Shyly he began his overtures with the new men, and presently at the free hours there gathered about him a little group. His talks were simple, full of the love of God and of charity.

"He has the rare gift of imparting peace," they said, one to another.

But when December dawned and talk of ordinations again filled the air, Francis felt the return of the familiar malaise. At these ordinations of 1830 some of his friends were to receive the subdeaconship. Their talk and preparations brought vividly to his memory the event which had occurred a year before, on the eve of ordinations—the event which had so drastically interrupted his life, leaving him in an indefinite state of suspension.

Nervously, he safeguarded himself, careful not to appear in public when the danger signals flashed. At length he began to feel better and congratulated himself that his caution, and the self-imposed rest, had routed the enemy. So it fell out that on the evening before the ceremony, when bad weather had kept the seminarians indoors, he was walking in the recreation hall with a group of his new friends. Suddenly, and this time without warning, the enemy struck. It was a major seizure—one of the worst he had ever suffered. He awakened in the infirmary, and as usual his only regret was for the shock and pain he had caused others. Would those new young men whom the Superior wanted him to help return to him? It was doubtful. . . .

Meantime, in the Superior's office, a dialogue was in progress.

"It was one of the worst seizures he has ever had," explained Dr. Lombard, "and this time it came without warning. And—what may be significant—precisely on the eve of ordinations, at the exact time when he was first stricken a year ago."

"Could that not be a mere coincidence?" asked Father Garnier.

"Yes," said the doctor slowly, but without much conviction. He paused, and gazed out of the window with puzzled eyes, as though searching for words to express a thought that remained uncrystallized.

"You know, *mon père*," he finally said, "I have had many talks with young Libermann since he was first stricken. His case interests me as much as it baffles me. In the course of these talks I have become greatly attached to him. Here is no ordinary soul, no ordinary mind. But no! He has revealed to me much of his past: of his youth and early training, of his father—oh, very much of his father!"

"The unappeased rabbi?" suggested Father Garnier.

"Exactly. Your young Jewish seminarian had an unusually deep devotion for his father. He admired him extravagantly, and when he was a child desired to emulate him in all things."

"Well, he certainly outgrew that," observed Father Garnier.

"Yes. But—" The doctor paused reflectively. Then he plunged on: "I've been wondering," he said, "whether there may be some connection between the man's feeling for his father, and these seizures. The Rabbi opposed his adoption of Christianity bitterly; that, coupled with his entry into a seminary, brought down upon him his father's curse."

"Medieval!" protested the Superior. "Surely a man of young Libermann's intelligence—"

"I don't know," interrupted the other. "He possesses a superior intelligence, to be sure, yet to a soul as sensitive as his —I am wondering. It may well be sheer coincidence that two of his worst seizures occurred immediately before ordinations —last year indeed, when he himself was to be ordained. But the other idea provides an interesting speculation. Mind you, there's no scientific basis for it! And I'm speaking to you in confidence. I would not like to be quoted."

"Of course not," said Father Garnier. "I shall mention it to no one."

"You see," went on Lombard, "science holds itself strictly aloof from recognizing any relationship between man's physical ills and his psychology. But I cannot escape the feeling that eventually the day may come when this will change. When, let us say, an emotion as elemental as fear will be an acknowledged factor in inducing an epileptic seizure—coupled with other elements, physical and nervous, of course."

Suddenly the good doctor looked horrified.

"I beg of you again, *mon père,* not to quote me. I have never spoken of this to anyone before."

Father Garnier leaned forward and placed a reassuring hand on his friend's arm.

"Your secret is safe with me," he smiled. "Moreover, it's very interesting. Let us both observe young Libermann even more carefully. In his case, I want above all things to act wisely. And let us beseech the good God for guidance." . . .

On the day when Francis was able to leave his bed, he ventured outdoors, having waited for an hour when he was sure all others would be in the lecture rooms. There was a white bandage drawn across his forehead, placed there by the doctor to cover the deep cut he had received when he had fallen against the sharp corner of a marble statue. Best, if he should remain out of sight for a few days. He felt extremely weak as he sat there on the bench, his eyes on a distant hill and naming over to himself those who had just been ordained. Suddenly a step sounded on the path. He looked up. To his amazement, there stood Bernard Tellier, the exhorter from the seminary of Stanislas. Not since the Abbé Augé had picked him up and carried him off to Stanislas for a rest during the summer of 1829—now more than a year ago—had he seen Bernard.

"Ah, Francis," cried Tellier, extending a hand, "I sought you in the infirmary and was told I might find you here."

"Bernard! It's good to see you. Come and sit down, and tell me all about Stanislas and what brings you here."

"I came," explained Bernard, dropping onto the bench, "on an errand of some importance—for our Superior." He seemed to swell a little. "I carried highly important documents, confidential in their nature, to Father Garnier." He paused significantly. "I think I may say that the Superior took me into his confidence; but naturally I am not at liberty to divulge the matter to anyone else."

"Naturally," said Francis gently, and successfully hiding his amusement.

"Of course I asked about you. News of your malady reached Stanislas some time ago. There, many prayers have been offered for you."

"I am most grateful," murmured Francis.

A note of true sincerity crept into Bernard's voice when he said:

"I am very sorry, Francis."

"Thank you, my friend. But do not be sorry. Rather rejoice with me that God has sent this affliction to test my love for Him."

"True. But you must view it also in a practical sense."

Francis steeled himself. The exhorter was rising to the surface.

"Yes?"

"You will, of course, leave the seminary?"

"I—I don't know, yet."

"You don't know? Why Francis, you should know by this time! Obviously, the priesthood is not for you. You remember that long ago I had doubts of it. Now I am certain. These seizures are God's means of telling you."

"At times it would indeed seem so," agreed Francis, unhappily.

"I sought you out today especially to help strengthen your resolve," went on Bernard sententiously, "for of course you must leave Saint-Sulpice. You must forever give up the idea of the priesthood. You must seek employment in the outside world."

"But it is for the priesthood alone that I have been trained."

"No matter. You are still young. Now, as your friend, I want to help you." Bernard leaned forward eagerly.

"It's very good of you."

"I have already spoken to my father," continued the other importantly. "He will give you a post on his farm, even though

he knows all about your malady. He needs someone to look
after the bookkeeping and accounts. You will have other
duties, too: supervising the help, purchasing equipment and
supplies. And oh, yes: feeding the stock—chickens, pigs,
cows—and of course helping with the harvests. In time, you
will begin to understand farming and will be advanced. My
father is pleased with the idea that you have been a seminarian and thus accustomed to early rising."

A chill ran up and down Francis' spine. He had never considered any career for himself but that of the priesthood,
whether of the synagogue or the Church—but he knew that
if he ever had, farming would have been the last.

"May I write him to expect you at the start of the New
Year?" pressed Bernard.

Francis looked miserable.

"Believe me, Bernard, I appreciate your kindness more
than I can say."

"Then you will go?"

"No. . . . I cannot."

The other drew back in astonishment.

"But why?"

"Because in spite of all appearances, in spite of your con-
victions which I well understand, I must remain here until
God tells me what He wants of me. He called me to His
priesthood. If He desires me to wait for a time, He has His
reasons."

Offended, Bernard rose from the bench.

"If you will not listen to a friend who wishes to help—" he
began stiffly.

"Oh please, dear Bernard; do not be offended."

"I will leave you to give further thought to what I have

said," replied the unmollified Bernard. "And I will pray that, for the first time in your life, you will begin to exercise a little common sense."

With that parting shaft he was gone. But he was scarcely out of sight before Francis, shaken and tremulous, had fled to the chapel—to that other, misunderstood One who hung suffering upon His cross. . . .

Yet for all his prayers, somehow Bernard's words continued to depress him; and his carefully hidden despair became deep indeed when, upon resuming appearances at recreation hours, many of the new young friends avoided him with studied excuses. Father Garnier, who seemed to have eyes everywhere, observed this; and the doctor having assured him that Francis, so recently stricken, would very likely be immune for a time, the Superior sent for the epileptic.

The summons reached Francis during the seminarians' midday meal. Rising quietly from his place, he hoped that his face did not portray the inner perturbation he felt. This would surely be the long-dreaded expulsion. Of course, after the last shameful seizure, the seminary could no longer keep him. As he hurried to the appointment, he nervously fingered the white bandage he still wore, the badge of an epileptic— silent but eloquent testimony that he was unworthy of the priesthood. By the time he had reached the door he could scarcely summon strength to knock. But to his relief, Father Garnier only extended to him a sheaf of documents.

"These must be returned to Stanislas," he explained, "and I will be grateful if you will carry them there for me. Take the day off, and spend some hours with your old friend and counselor, the Abbé Augé."

Francis could only stutter his thanks. Father Garnier had

guessed his need of talking with the Abbé. On his part, Francis guessed that the documents he was to return were the very same as those which Bernard had so importantly carried to Saint-Sulpice. Odd, that the Superior made no attempt to impress him with their importance. . . .

"In addition," Father Garnier was continuing, "I would like you to conduct a visitor there. He is waiting in the next room, a young man who came to me this morning for advice. I have a feeling that the Abbé Augé can help him more than I. He is in great sadness, having recently lost both parents and a sister in a terrible fire which demolished their home. As you go, try to help him with your own counsel. And tell the Abbé that I will appreciate his good offices in this respect."

The Superior also suggested that before proceeding to Stanislas, they might visit the Cathedral of Notre Dame.

"It is our young friend's first visit to Paris," he explained, "and of course he should see it."

So it transpired that Francis, clad in civilian garb—since it was considered unsafe in these troubled times for anyone to appear in the streets of Paris wearing a soutane—set off with the documents in his pocket, and the inconsolable young Henri de Motte at his side. He was thinking of Father Garnier's great charity in continuing him at Saint-Sulpice. He wondered how long it could last—for after all, both of them owed an obligation to the Archbishop of Paris whose purse maintained him there in the expectation that he would one day serve as an ordained priest. In his present depressed state, such an eventuality seemed out of the question.

It was a day chilled by rain and fog; sodden skies wept over Paris. His companion's despair matched their mood, and as he unfolded without reservation his triple tragedy, Francis was hard put to it to uplift the heart of his confidant. Eventually as they made their way, they approached a bridge over the Seine which they must traverse. Quite suddenly Francis felt incapable of the task imposed upon him. Who was he to bring solace to another, when his own heart was breaking? For the moment forgetting his companion, he dropped into silence, overcome by melancholy. What was he doing here anyway, playing the role of a son of Saint-Sulpice? He had no right to that position. He had been cast off as unwanted. In a flash, all of Bernard's words came tumbling into his mind. . . . "You must forever give up the idea of priesthood. . . . You must seek employment in the outside world." But where, how? He was imposing on Father Garnier, on his companions at Saint-Sulpice, above all, on his Archbishop, by lingering at the seminary.

All at once he was conscious that they were on the bridge. He felt his eyes drawn down to the muddy, turbulent river below. Suddenly he thought, "Were I quickly to jump, there in those waters I could find swift peace; there I could end the burden on others—on myself. All would be better off—and the All-Understanding God would be merciful." Abruptly he halted.

"What is it?" asked Henri, stopping. "Does your shoe hurt you?"

Francis pulled himself erect with difficulty.

"No—not my shoe," he assured the other slowly. Then, summoning a smile, he resumed his stride.

"When you stopped, I had just been thinking," said Henri, "that it's all very well for you to assure me that God loves me and holds me in His care, when you yourself have probably never undergone any sorrow. One can tell from your smile alone that you have never suffered." . . .

Later, when Francis was at last alone in the chapel of Stanislas, he buried his head in his hands and wept.

"To think that I was on the point of betraying You, my Jesus! Forgive, forgive! That most heinous of all sins tempted me. Can I ever make amends?" . . .

He did not tell the Abbé Augé. He was too ashamed. But following the episode, he shunned the river and its bridges— his soul stricken with terror at the thought of the temptation which might ensue.

One man alone was aware of the thoughts that had assaulted him there on the bridge—his confessor at Saint-Sulpice, Father Faillon. From the moment he learned of them, the scientist-priest kept himself informed of his penitent's state of health. When there was a temporary surcease from seizures, he made a point of asking Francis to serve at his daily Mass at the near-by Church of Saint-Sulpice—whose saintly parish priest, John Jacob Olier, had in 1642 founded the Sulpician Society under whose direction the seminary functioned.

It fell out that on the first day of May the church was crowded with those who had come to honor her to whom the month is dedicated. Father Faillon was on the altar, and Francis, the humble acolyte, was serving. Midway in the throng knelt the young daughter of the de Montforts, scarcely sixteen, and with a face like a flower. She had come with her parents to the early service in order to receive the Sacrament, as the day was doubly significant for her. It was not only the beginning of the month of Our Lady, but later on this day, at

a special ceremony in the convent she attended, young
Thérèse would be received as a Child of Mary, and consecrated to the Mother of God.

With great recollection, the young heart replete with devotion, Thérèse bowed her head at the Consecration. Lifting
it again moments later, she was stricken with fear and half
rose from her *prie-dieu*.

"*Maman*," she whispered, touching her mother's arm,
"Look! The acolyte—he is on fire!"

Quickly the Baroness turned her eyes to the devout figure
kneeling behind the priest. She saw nothing unusual. Patting
her daughter's hand, she gently forced her back to her knees.

"Hush, my dear. You are overwrought," she whispered.

But Thérèse did not hear. She was gazing spellbound at the
acolyte, about whose head there glowed a luminous aureole,
meeting and merging in a tongue of flame which parted directly above his forehead. She could not understand why he
seemed quite unconscious of it. It must be burning him. Then,
when he moved and she caught sight of his profile, suddenly
a picture and lines from her Bible flashed into her mind:
"When the days of the Pentecost were accomplished . . .
there appeared to them parted tongues as it were of fire, and
it sat upon every one of them. . . ."

Why, the profile of the acolyte looked like one of those in
the steel engraving opposite that passage. He—he looked like
a Jew. The flame about his head gave a singular beauty to that
face. . . . Then, all at once, Thérèse knew that the young
man on the altar, whom she had never seen before, was an
apostle. Later, she would learn who he was; later, she would
find a means of knowing him. . . .

As the year passed at Saint-Sulpice and a chill November

drew on, it had become evident to all that Francis' malady was not a thing of temporary character. Father Garnier was sorely perplexed. The sanctity of the victim, the benefit of his example and his spiritual influence over others, were abundantly evident; but only the other day he had suffered another bad seizure, and once more the fine brow bore a white badge covering a large bruise.

Francis awakened on the seventh day of November with a very heavy heart. It was not that the danger signals were flying, he reflected as he dressed hastily to serve the early Mass, but that an unusual depression weighed upon him. He had a leaden sense of some nameless, imminent misfortune. While the glory of the Sacrifice restored his peace, as it always did, nevertheless as the day wore on, the premonition reasserted itself. Then at noon came the summons. He was wanted in the Superior's office. Although on each of the previous occasions he had dreaded expulsion, this time he knew overwhelmingly and without shadow of doubt that it was here. Yet surprisingly, this was the one time that he felt the strength to meet it. He was able to approach the familiar door with a firm step.

When he had entered, he found to his surprise not Father Garnier but his assistant, Father Carbon. Little did Francis guess that the Superior had felt himself unequal to the interview.

Father Carbon's words were very kind. The Council of Saint-Sulpice had long been considering his case. They had held frequent consultations with his doctor and studied with the concern of a father for a son the medical record of his seizures from the time they had first begun, at the close of the year 1829. It was now approaching the close of 1831; but unhappily the two years' record, despite mandatory rest, despite the lightest possible schedule of studies, did not suggest any hope of cure. Meantime, due to the civil disturbances of 1830, the seminary had suffered not only financially, but also somewhat in prestige. It had not been safe for the seminarians to appear as such in Paris. This had necessitated a relaxed discipline. The time had come when no question of the seminary's administration must be raised—a question which might easily be inspired by malicious tongues concerning the retention of one who was probably forever barred from the priesthood. The Archbishop's funds were not limitless. The purse which he had generously bestowed for the tuition and maintenance of Francis should, in all justice, be transferred to an applicant of sound health but slender means—of whom there were many.

Francis stood with bowed head. There was a moment's silence. At length he spoke:

"I understand, *mon père*," he said softly. "Saint-Sulpice has been very good to me. The Council is right in reaching such a decision."

Inwardly he was praying. ("Thy Will be done! But from Thy Infinite Mercy, show me, show me the way.")

"The Council is of the opinion," Father Carbon was continuing, "that you must abandon all thought of the priesthood, and should now consider ways by which you can support yourself in the outside world. We will help you as far as is possible—but have you any thoughts yourself, on this subject?"

"No, *mon père*," replied the acolyte. "And I cannot have, until it is made clear what God desires of me. He has privileged me by the bestowal of minor orders—it has made me feel that I can never return to the world. But I understand and accept the decision of Saint-Sulpice. I will ask God to direct me. Surely He will let me know what He wishes of me; and most certainly He will not abandon me."

As he spoke an uncomfortable look passed over Father Carbon's face: He was thinking: "What stupidity of mine! Yet the logic of my argument was perfect. . . . What is there about logic, anyway? At times, it can be so completely unsatisfying. . . ." But he said nothing.

Francis, expressing his infinite gratitude for all the seminary had done for him, quietly took his leave; and as he did so, he bestowed upon the priest one of his sunniest smiles.

Feeling a tightness in his throat, Father Carbon gazed regretfully at the slender disappearing figure. That white bandage on the nobly proportioned head. . . . He sighed deeply as the door closed.

CHAPTER TEN

The Call

THERE WAS NO DOUBT that some of the younger seminarians had got out of hand. The donning of secular attire for excursions into Paris and during summer holidays, made necessary by the civil disturbances of the years 1830 to 1832, had been a factor. The age-old psychological effect of costume, both upon those who wear it and those who behold it, was not absent in the France of that day, especially not in the aristocratic circles to which many of the seminarians by right belonged.

Without the soutane, when the young men moved in the outside world, it was easy for them to forget, if for the moment, the career for which they were being trained. To forget it was even easier for their friends. Pious, but at the same time doting and short-sighted mothers insisted upon costly attire for these favored sons who would one day bring glory to the family name by their dedication to the priesthood.

It had been just such a mother, a member of the old nobility, who had one day visited the Superior of Saint-Sulpice to congratulate him in all good faith on his "liberal" policy with the young men.

"I'm delighted to see," she said, "the seminarists walking in Paris, and have remarked with pleasure that several are often followed by their footmen in livery."

The mild lady was surprised to see the Superior start from his chair and clutch his head. . . .

He knew that not all young men who enter a seminary remain to walk the disciplined path and to complete the long and arduous years of study. The gate is straight and narrow, and grace is not always bestowed. Mistaken vocations are not infrequent with idealistic and impetuous youth. But the Superior could not fail to recognize that more of the beginners were now leaving during their first year of study than had formerly been the case.

The matter of attire alone was serious enough to weaken discipline, thought the Council of Saint-Sulpice; but when to it was added the confusion resultant upon the terrible cholera epidemic of 1832, sometimes they wondered if they would ever be able to restore that aloofness from the world which must be the cornerstone in the training of all priests.

Cholera had struck the gay capital in the month of March. For seven months Paris lay prostrate under this scourge which, before it had subsided, had taken a toll of more than twenty thousand lives. Father Garnier had immediately placed the seminary at the disposal of the Ministry of Health, and had opened wide its doors to the sick and the dying. These had arrived by the hundreds. The seminarians themselves were given a choice of returning to their own homes, or of seeking shelter in the country seminary at Issy—the Solitude. But from among them all, the Superior had called for thirty volunteers to remain at the Paris house to serve as nurses and infirmarians during the epidemic.

When the tragic story was told, Saint-Sulpice had won a record of heroic selflessness unequaled in the annals of Paris —but its precious discipline had been scattered to the four winds. Some satisfactions however remained to the anxious Father Garnier. His heroic thirty had saved hundreds of lives —only forty-two of the stricken had died within his walls. Hundreds had been baptized or restored to an abandoned faith; and thanks to the great mercy of God, not a single seminarian, either in Paris or at Issy, had been smitten by the terrible scourge. This in itself was a miracle.

When he began to gather his scattered flock about him, it was small wonder that his gravest problem was the restoration of an ordered life and the winning back to totally spiritual concepts of those who had been caught up involuntarily in the whirl of the temporal. How was he to revive the spirit of the saintly Father Olier who had founded the society expressly to train young men for the sacred priesthood? Or of the late Calixte Frèze, "the angel of Sisteron," who had so recently evoked the breath of the Spirit within the old halls of Saint-Sulpice? Should not the attempt be made particularly at the Solitude, that quiet retreat of the students of philosophy? It seemed to him also that it should take the form of a movement among the students themselves. . . .

Three years had passed. The October of 1835 had been generous with its warm colors to the hilltop of Issy; nor had it spared its mellow sunshine. Young Charles Maigna of the magnificent head, the tall strong body, and the flashing black eyes had startled both Saint-Sulpice and the Solitude with his genius for mathematics. It was said that even when in chapel he had difficulty in restraining himself from working out mathematical formulae upon his fingers. On a certain day during this October he had left the Superior's office, and in his exuberance had cleared the stairs of the Solitude three at a time. Thundering down the hall to the room of his classmate, Jean Robert, and flinging open the door, he had cried:

"*Allons, citoyen!* We are off to Paris, you and I. I have the Father Superior's permission to attend the lecture at the Sorbonne this afternoon—that new German economist, the greatest mathematician in Europe! You are to accompany me, as nursemaid."

Jean, who had looked up from his books as the approaching steps had shaken the floor, grinned and shook his head.

"Not I, my friend. Get someone else. Granted that you require such care as is needed by an infant. But I cannot be your nurse this afternoon. There is a previous engagement."

Thunderclouds engulfed the other's handsome face.

"*Ciel!* You mean, you would miss this great opportunity?" Jean cast a side glance at the crucifix on his wall.

"I would," he replied, smilingly but firmly. "I have other fish to fry."

"What fish?" demanded Maigna, throwing himself on the bed. "Don't tell me that you have become involved in the pious walks and talks of that flighty Libermann?"

"The same," said Jean quietly. "Only—he's not flighty."

"What!" cried Maigna. "You too are bitten? You, one of the best scientists at the seminary! I can't believe it."

"I couldn't myself, at first," rejoined the other. "But one day I happened to be reading on that far-off bench just by the park. Libermann emerged from the trees with a group of

followers. I could not fail to hear what he was saying. . . .
It was—very impressive."

"Oh, my poor friend," moaned Maigna, "that you too
should have been trapped by all this moonstruck mysticism!
It's outrageous, that's what it is. The man ought to be sent
away. He's a menace to the Solitude."

"He may, rather, be its saviour," commented the other
softly.

Enraged, Charles pulled himself to a sitting position and
regarded his friend sternly.

"It's all schoolgirl hypnotism," he said, "those long talks
and walks—these so-called 'bands of piety.' They are ruining
our best scientific minds by shackling attention to a half-
baked mysticism. I've seen it happen to others. Just when the
science courses are beginning to scintillate with brains, lo,
another Libermann addict is made! And instead of putting
his mind on the laboratory, he is mooning about the grounds
with the other half-wits discussing theological theorems
which can never be proved. It's a disease—a dangerous contagion."

"Come and see for yourself," urged his friend. "Come this
afternoon."

"Not I," said the other, rising in disgust. "I'm off to the Sorbonne with someone who is still in his right mind—if I can
find one around this place. Why, Jean, don't you understand?
This Libermann is an epileptic. He's not even a priest. And
any scientific man will tell you that epileptics are weak-
minded. The disease dulls and destroys the faculties of the
brain. That a man who is so mentally afflicted should be encouraged to lead others astray, is a reflection on the intellectual caliber of those who direct Saint-Sulpice. What the

Church needs today is not a vague mysticism of inaction, but an aggressive conquest of science in the active new world science is building. We are not living in the Middle Ages, my friend. I have half a mind to go to the authorities and demand that Libermann be ousted."

And with thunder still upon his brow, Maigna slammed from the room. . . .

Meanwhile, the subject of their discussion was sitting quietly in an arbor at the end of one of the trimly hedged walks which were characteristic of the Solitude. He was awaiting the arrival of two young men, newcomers to Issy, who had requested an interview with him. He could never come to this arbor without recalling vividly the morning when the cannons had boomed over Paris, and his heart had seemed to break because no one was thinking of God.

Francis looked somewhat older than he had on the day, now almost four years ago, when he had thought he was bidding farewell to all seminary life. He smiled tenderly as he sat there reflecting on the great goodness of God. For God had ordained quite otherwise. On that momentous November noon when he had left Father Carbon's office facing expulsion, he recalled that he had felt almost light of heart. It was that odd relief of knowing at last a fate which had long been feared. Certainty of disaster had been easier to bear than its long-endured expectation.

He had gone to his small room to pack up his few belongings, thinking that Felkel would be greatly surprised to see him—surprised and upset. He must hasten with his packing so there would be time for a last long visit to his dear refuge, the chapel. Ah, the chapel! How would things be without it, there in the outside world? Then had come the knock upon his door. He must take himself in hand, to present a cheerful front. He had guessed it would be Georges, or Salier, or Jarrier. But no. The door had opened, and there had stood Father Carbon himself, looking slightly embarrassed.

"My dear Francis," he had said, "I have just finished reporting our interview to the members of the Council. To my joy I am able to tell you that the Council has unanimously reversed its decision. It invites you to remain with us. True, you may no longer enjoy the Archbishop's purse—but other ways will be found. Father Superior highly values your work with the younger men, but he thinks that your health will be better at Issy, than here in Paris. He advises that you remove to the Solitude. There, of course, we shall see you frequently."

Tears of gratitude . . . and with them he had just stood there, unable to utter a word. Softly Father Carbon had retired. . . .

The exquisite charity of the Superior, in planning for his health! The quiet and remoteness here, the pure air, had wrought marvels. They had not banished his "dear malady" completely, but now the seizures came at much longer intervals. It had been many months now since one had visited him. Gradually he had been able to resume his studies in philosophy.

Immediately upon his arrival they had set him to working out of doors—cleaning the walks, raking the lawns, tending the garden. He had accepted with joy the most menial tasks, happy beyond all that his shelter was a house devoted to God. How would it have fared with him—he upon whom minor orders had been bestowed—had he been forced to live in a world where God was counted of such small concern?

But as for his attaining to the priesthood, at Issy his conviction had grown that he was not worthy. All he had to do was to think of Francis of Assisi, his patron saint, to whom he was devoted. If that great Saint, "the Little Poor Man," had throughout life deemed himself unworthy of this privilege, what wild fatuousness had ever possessed him, Francis Libermann, with the notion that he was worthy? He was glad and grateful just to be permitted to serve those who were.

Strange, how he had fallen into the role of counselor here. When he had arrived, broken in health, bewildered as to his destiny, he had not dreamed that he would ever be able to resume such talks as Father Garnier had asked him to conduct at Saint-Sulpice. At first he had begun them quite by accident, in the infirmary when recovering from an attack, and when others who also lay ill had opened up discussion— soon they were asking him about many things; and then with the servants, with whom his work threw him—and particularly with that very holy old man who served as porter.

When the cholera had laid siege to Paris, he had longed with all his heart to volunteer for the sick and dying at Saint-Sulpice—but he knew only too well that he would have been rejected. (Think of the poor cholera victims, forced to witness their infirmarian in the throes of an epileptic seizure!) But from newcomers who constantly arrived from the Paris house, he had eagerly gleaned all the details of that work of Christian heroism—and had been greatly moved by the tale.

But he had been as concerned as the Superior himself with the disorganized discipline—and when it had been proposed that he should assist in stimulating the "bands of piety," he had thrown himself into the task with great fervor. Soon thereafter their success had begun to exceed even the Council's fondest expectations. It was true that not all the seminarians

had participated. There were many like Maigna who, fired
by the contemporary discoveries which were spiraling exact
science to the top of men's minds, were impatient of the in-
exact science of mysticism. Active members of the bands were
in the minority—but they formed a source of power stronger
than any produced in the seminary's laboratories. Among the
rest they served as catalysts. A new spirit had come to reign
at the Solitude and Saint-Sulpice. Smart civilian attire was
seen less frequently. The footmen in livery had vanished.

Each band was purposely small; each had its own discussion leader. The topics were introduced as the young men
walked under the open sky, or sat beneath the whispering
loveliness of the great trees. Gradually, and almost without
anyone being conscious of it, the epileptic "Father" Libermann, as all the seminarians now called him, had become the
central figure about whom the bands revolved.

As Francis waited in the arbor to keep his appointment on
that golden October afternoon, he reflected that the two newcomers who had requested it were also affected by contemporary world events—though not in the same manner as the
science enthusiasts. The French conquest of Algiers in 1830
had opened up new channels of commerce and information.
It had set the spiritual world to stirring with a sense of pity,
and of obligation to the world's neglected and exploited
dark-skinned children. What had been done about bearing
the message of Christ to these? The two young men whom he
now awaited, and who were members of the bands, were eloquent on the subject.

Both were Creoles—not of Negro extraction, but born of
descendants of French colonists who had mated with other
Latins in the islands of Haiti and Bourbon. Francis had a

particular sympathy for these two. Both in their early twenties, they looked up to the gentle-faced "Father" Libermann, now thirty-three, as to an older brother. Each had won his stay in the seminary after a hard battle with health—even as had he. They were Creoles, he was a Jew—facts which, regardless of all good will, could not fail to set them apart in a certain sense from their fellows. The handsome Frederic Le Vavasseur from the island of Bourbon in the Indian Ocean was both Creole and Jew; and since he, like Francis, had been forced to oppose a stern and unforgiving father in his aspirations for the priesthood, Francis felt a particular kinship with him.

He looked up now with a warm smile as their feet sounded on the path. It was young Eugene Tisserant from Haiti who spoke first. The large eyes flashed with earnestness.

"I have just received another appeal from those good men in Haiti who are deeply concerned about conditions there. Again they have implored me to make known to the authorities here the pitiable state of the Negroes. It is growing more deplorable every day, due to the persistent lack of good missionary priests. I beg you, Father, to advise me. For I cannot fail them!"

"And I," said Le Vavasseur, "have just had further word from my beloved mother in Bourbon. She relates the same conditions there. Ah, how often have I myself witnessed them! It is impossible to describe the wretched state of the poor Negroes—a state worse than the lowest type of slavery. As I have told you, people in France have no idea. I feel impelled to do something, Father, for these poor souls—I love them," he added simply.

Tisserant took up the plea.

"Frederic and I have been wondering if you would join us—"

"We wish to form a sort of new missionary society," burst in Le Vavasseur. "And we need you."

Francis, taken aback, looked his surprise and began to shake his head. Le Vavasseur dropped on the bench beside him and leaned forward eagerly:

"You could do it, Father. You could lead it, that is. And Eugene and I would help. You would be wonderful at it. Others would surely be drawn—for people everywhere are aroused by the revelations that have come out of Africa. In America, countless good people have already freed their slaves, believing as we that human slavery is a sin before the Face of Christ. Eugene and I want to help the Negroes of our own homelands. Please join us, Father."

Francis replied with great gentleness:

"My good friends, your zeal is beautiful. It would seem that God has given you the true missionary vocation. And with you, my heart bleeds for the poor Negroes, enslaved by those who call themselves Christians but who have never revealed to them the sweetness of Christ. But, my friends, we must first of all be practical. You two are yet in training for the priesthood. I am no more than a humble acolyte. How far do you think we three *unordained* ones would get, trying to launch a society of mission priests? Surely, we must wait!"

"But Father, the time is now. New and terrible insurrections threaten—bloodshed, such as we have known only too well in Haiti," exclaimed Tisserant. "We cannot afford to wait!"

"My dear friends," said Francis, "what did we speak of the other day concerning the patience that is so pleasing to God?

Trusting Him completely, as we do, we can wait, in all love."

"Does that mean that you will be unwilling to discuss the idea further with us?" asked Le Vavasseur anxiously.

"Not at all. You are my cherished friends—members of the bands. At all times you must come to me when you feel the need to talk. Gather all the information possible about conditions at home, and put it down in writing. We shall discuss frequently. And we shall pray much. Then some day, if and when God pleases, we may be permitted to employ that information in spreading His kingdom upon the good earth He created."

He was very practical, was Father Libermann, agreed the two, as comforted if also crestfallen, they left him to join the strolling band which Jean Robert was leading that day. . . .

There were others, too, at the Solitude who had found the humble acolyte to be "very practical." Chiefly, the Superior. On the day following Francis' conversation with the two friends, Father Mollevaut, waiting in his office to see the acolyte, was reflecting how he had discovered it quite by accident. He smiled now as he recalled the event which had "promoted" Libermann into the post of the seminary's favorite commissionaire. Francis had been at Issy for more than a year before anyone had dreamed of considering him fit to conduct business negotiations—until that summer day three years ago.

The Superior could see the scene as though it had been enacted but yesterday. He had been annoyed, he recalled, when the cook had reported that the seminarian commissioned to order a cartload of vegetables from the public market in Paris had forgotten all about it. There would be none on hand for the next meal, and there was not time to send anyone back to Paris. In his perplexity he had glanced out the window and his eye had chanced to fall upon the slender figure raking the lawn. Calling Francis to him, he had directed him from the open window:

"Go to the nearest farmstead and buy a quantity of vegetables—cabbages, onions, beans—as many as the farmer will sell. They do not like to sell to us, preferring to take their products to the city market. So the farmer will try to charge you a very fancy price. You will just have to pay it, for the cook is desperate, with nothing for dinner!"

"What would they cost in the city market, *mon père?*"

"A hundred francs—that is the amount I'm giving you—would be sufficient to buy a generous supply. But I doubt if you will get barely enough for one meal, especially if you deal with our neighbor, Pierre Olivant. Moreover, you will have to ask him to deliver them at once, as there is need of haste."

With some misgivings he had watched Libermann start down the path toward the gates. His step was firm; but would he be safe, he wondered, even on a country road? Murmuring a prayer for him, Father Mollevaut had retraced his steps to the office, only to find an urgent message calling him at once to the village. So it happened that within ten minutes, he too had started down the path. As he approached the gates, he could hear a lively dialogue taking place just beyond. He recognized the quiet, amiable voice as Libermann's, and the rapid, excited tones of the other were vaguely familiar. Then he had come upon an odd sight.

A farmer's cart headed toward the city had lost a wheel just opposite the seminary entrance. Pitched at an angle, most of its produce was strewn in profusion across the dusty road.

The old horse, released from his harness, was placidly munching the grass at one side; and the plump Pierre Olivant in his linen smock was casting forth imprecations as he stooped to gather into a heap his good vegetables. Francis was smilingly helping him. The Superior remained unobserved, watching the scene.

"Just as I was on my way to draw a fine price for these in the city market!" bemoaned the farmer. "Now I shall have to walk into the village for the wheelwright. Even if he can come at once, it will take time to replace the wheel—and I will have lost my place in the market."

"What do you expect to make from this load, once you get to the market?" asked Francis casually, as he carefully dusted off a fine cabbage.

"A good deal more than a hundred francs," avowed Pierre.

"But if your place in the market is gone?" questioned the other sympathetically.

Pierre clutched his head and gave loud vent to his distress.

"*Mille diables!*" he cried. "That's just it! I always have the best position. Now I shall have to snatch whatever is left. It will not be desirable, I can tell you that!"

"It's a great pity," said Francis consolingly. "You will probably be very late, too, getting home."

Pierre clutched his head again.

"And oh, how my old woman will scold! Late, and with less in my pocket than she expects."

"My poor friend," sympathized the acolyte, tossing a sheaf of onions onto the heap. "I should like to help you."

"No one can help me now but the wheelwright," complained the farmer, as he made to start off down the road.

"Wait a moment," said Francis. "What would you think if you were offered sixty francs for the load? For the seminary, that is—"

Pierre stopped as though hit by a shot in the back. Wheeling about, he cried with a look of mortal insult:

"*Sixty francs?* Are you mad, my poor Abbé? I'm not in business for charity!"

"It's a pity that you cannot recognize a good offer," said Francis quietly, dusting his hands from the last cabbage. "Our Father Superior might be generous enough to pay sixty francs, even if there is damage—as there certainly is here."

"Damage!" shrieked Pierre, his body taut as from a death sentence. Then attempting a slow dignity, he had swaggered back to the heap. "Why, there's not a blemish!"

Carefully he picked up a cabbage in such a manner that the bruise did not show. "See! It's flawless!"

Francis shrugged. "Sixty francs," he said indifferently.

Pierre walked over to him and shook his finger under the thin, ascetic profile.

"I can get twice that much in Paris, this very day. Do you take me for a simpleton?"

"Arriving late? And your place gone?"

"You are only trying to torment me!" shouted Pierre. "I tell you, I will get more than twice."

"And had you thought, my friend," suggested Francis, "that you may have to wait some time for the wheelwright?"

"You are only trying to make me miserable—you, a man of religion!"

"Just think—how easy to dispose of the lot here. You would not even have to deliver them. Our young men would carry them in."

"But sixty francs! It's robbery!" He turned his back determinedly and started off again. Suddenly he paused, turning a reluctant head.

"Surely the seminary is not so poor? Surely you could offer more? Men of religion should be ashamed—"

"Tell me this," interrupted Francis, "how much will you have to pay the wheelwright?"

"All of ten francs," almost sobbed Pierre, "for he, too, is a robber."

"Thank you, my friend," smiled Francis. "But I have an idea. We have a wheelwright at the seminary, a very skilled one. Now, as you say, the job is worth ten francs—"

"I did not say it's worth ten francs," exploded Pierre. "I said the robber would charge that."

"Exactly," soothed Francis. "Now, if the Father Superior were to be very generous and offer you sixty-five francs for the load, and we were to repair your wheel without charge— thereby saving you ten francs—that would really make your profit a total of seventy-five francs, would it not? A very handsome offer for a load of damaged vegetables."

Pierre seemed suspended in a misery of doubt.

"Such a hot day for that long walk," commiserated Francis. "But the other way, you could have your cart mended while you wait. And think how you will surprise your wife by an early return. And how pleasant she will be, as you drive into the barn the richer by seventy-five francs."

"It's piracy, but I surrender," sighed Pierre, sitting down by the roadside. Then he quickly added: "But you will not carry the vegetables off until I see my cart repaired!"

"But naturally not," assured Francis, as he started for the gates. "I will return at once with our man."

"And remember," called out Pierre in virtuous tones, "I only consent to this because you serve *le Bon Dieu!*"

Francis turned and said solemnly: "But, of course!" He did not permit himself to smile until his back was again turned.

Just within the gates he ran headlong into the Superior. Europe's most distinguished Greek scholar seemed to be having difficulty. Bent over, he was coughing violently into his handkerchief.

"I hope there's nothing wrong?" asked Francis solicitously.

"Nothing, nothing," said Father Mollevaut, his face very red. "I got to coughing just as I heard you conclude your bargain." His lips twitched, and then, much to the surprise of Francis, he had burst into an open laugh.

"Excellent!" he had said. "Now go fetch Denis to mend that wheel!" . . .

So on this October day the Superior was still chuckling at the recollection when Francis knocked at his door.

"Here is the list, commissionaire," he said genially. "Look it over and see if you have any questions."

Francis read it aloud rapidly: so much oil for the lamps, so much soap, so much meat, so many vegetables, so much wine for the altar, so many candles—

"Tomorrow is the Feast of St. Simon and St. Jude," interrupted Father Mollevaut, "and several men are coming from Saint-Sulpice for a day of recollection. They will be with us for dinner. Many will walk with the bands in the afternoon. So, if you have any money left,"—he thrust a handful of notes at Francis—"you might buy some cakes. The sort the young ones like. Although, with the list I've given you, I really can't see how there will be anything left."

Francis counted the notes carefully. "There will be something left, *mon père*," he assured the other.

"I don't doubt it," agreed Father Mollevaut with a broad grin. "That's why I'm sending *you*. Who was it who taught you to bargain, anyway?"

Francis was forced to laugh.

"I believe, *mon père*, that I was taught by a long line of ancestors."

"An ancient and distinguished line," said his superior. "I could do with a few more of you here!"

"Patience, *mon père*. You know I yet have a brother or two. Who can tell?"

"I've been thinking of that too—or at least of your seeing something of your family again. How would you like it if we could arrange to get you to Strasbourg next summer—and possibly on to Saverne, eh?"

The sensitive features flushed with pleasure and surprise.

"Oh!" was all Francis was able to say.

"Well, go on doing as well as you have done with the bands. I may tell you that Father Garnier, the Abbé Augé, and all your old friends at Saint-Sulpice, and Monsieur Drach as well, are delighted. And once the summer holiday starts—" He broke off, to add more seriously: "Depending upon your health, of course."

A radiant Libermann started off for Paris. To think of it! He might see Samson; and Babette—by letter he had become her unfailing spiritual counselor. The six children were growing. The youngest, a boy, would be one year old in January. Agnes Léa would now be ten; and little Marie, whose godfather he had become by proxy and who had been named at his suggestion, would soon be six. He knew he was loved in that household. Had not Babette, in her anxiety over his poverty, sent him some fine linen sheets for his bed? (Far too fine for him, he had thought, and had promptly turned them over to the poor. He hoped she would never know.) And had they not repeatedly written, pleading with him to visit them?

Only one thought marred the otherwise delightful prospect as he made his way about the city on the seminary's errands. It was the thought of Saverne—Saverne and the old house next to the synagogue. He had not told Father Mollevaut, but for some time he had known that he was no longer welcome there. David had finally left it, and was now working in Strasbourg where he spent much time with Samson and his family—an influence which was certain to have its effect. In the old house there remained only Sarah, the stepmother; and her children, Isaac and young Sarah. David had written him that his stepmother, once so devoted, had turned against him upon the death of his father. She held him accountable for it, as did his own brother Henoch. And she had brought up her children strictly and rigidly in the Old Law. Young Isaac, at twenty, would soon himself be officiating as a rabbi.

In a sense it was pathetic, reflected Francis with the inevitable heartache that accompanied every thought of his father. Only after the Rabbi Libermann was called to his ancestors had the wish that he had cherished all his life—that a son should follow in his path—come true. Of the six first sons, four were now Catholics. . . . No, he could not very well go to Saverne. And yet there was a special longing which drew him there. It was to see once again, the young half sister, Sarah, whom he remembered only as a lovable little girl. But he had heard from others that she frequently asked about him, and had wistfully expressed the desire to see him.

Later that day when he laid an accounting upon the Superior's desk, he felt satisfied with his purchases. Father Mollevaut was in chapel, but Francis left a note saying that he had been able to accomplish a saving on the candles and the soap, having luckily found a dealer on the Left Bank who was going out of business. So he had bought the cakes for the feast day tomorrow, and was returning a slight bit of change.

When he appeared in the recreation hall, there were five or six seminarians waiting to see him, each with a different problem. At last, when the busy day was done and he had made his final visit to the chapel, he retired with a happy heart. For a long time now, there had been no danger signals. He thanked his All Merciful Father.

The following day being gala, each who dined in the long refectory was permitted to choose his own place at table, friend sitting with friend. On such occasions he invariably stood back and waited quietly until all were seated, and then took whatever place was left. But today when that moment came, he saw to his dismay that the only vacant seat was one next to that of Charles Maigna, the mathematician. Francis knew very well how unpopular he was in that quarter. All the "scientists" were grouped at Maigna's end of the table, and it was well known in what contempt they held the bands of piety. Overcoming a temptation to flee and to miss his dinner entirely, he advanced quietly toward the empty place. Maigna looked up in surprise and quite obvious displeasure —a fact not lost upon his companions. It was evident at once that they considered the incident a great joke upon their friend, for they began to whisper and laugh among themselves.

"Pardon," said Francis softly to Maigna. "The fact is there was no other place."

The other regarded him sullenly. Just then there was a burst of laughter at some sally made by one of the students sitting directly opposite. It was too much for Maigna's dignity. Hurt in the first instance that none of his friends had chosen the place next to him, and infuriated at the sport at his expense, he turned to Francis with a scowl and said loudly:

"You! If you but knew how greatly I detest you!"

For an instant a quiver passed over the fine Semitic face. Then the dark eyes were turned steadily upon Maigna.

"And you," he said clearly, "if you but knew how greatly I love you."

The laughter at that end of the table was suddenly hushed. A scientist pushed a plate across to Francis, and said:

"Here, Father, you haven't any bread."

Another hastened to pass a platter of meat, while a third said:

"Let me pour some coffee for you, Father."

Maigna shoved his plate aside, untasted, and remained glumly silent for the balance of the meal. But when Francis, the last to leave the dining hall, entered the corridor, he found his antagonist awaiting him. The large frame seemed somehow to have shrunk—the flashing black eyes to have lost their fire.

"Father—I—I apologize."

The other extended a hand, smiling warmly.

"It is forgotten," he said.

"No," said Maigna, "it will never be forgotten—by me. But tell me, Father—what is the secret of your peace?" . . .

The two spent most of the afternoon together. And the next day all of the Solitude was electrified to learn that Maigna, the mathematician, the bitterest opponent of the bands of piety, had enlisted in their ranks.

Now as the days shortened and cold winds of the winter of 1836 whistled about the Issy hilltop, Francis began to feel the effects of his extended schedule upon his health. To his delight he had been permitted to resume full attendance in the philosophy courses. But to the study and to his intensive work with the bands, to his commissions in the city, had gradually been added a new duty. It was an extensive correspondence with those who had come in contact with him on their visits to Issy—not alone students, but priests. Many an older man had, even as Maigna, been moved to learn the secret of his peace. A benignity had come to rest upon the face of the acolyte which had the curious effect of stilling such fears and tempests as troubled the souls of those who looked into it. With great humility he had consented to guide these by word and by pen.

It had been five years since he had received his first letter from a stranger, asking for spiritual guidance. He had been at Saint-Sulpice, and the letter had come from the young Thérèse de Montfort who, following her strange vision in church on that first of May, had found her way to Francis by letter. Through the years she had written at intervals when troubled by a spiritual problem, and had never failed to receive a prompt and consoling reply. But all such correspondence was at the serious expense of his own rest.

Accordingly the danger signals flashed again; and although it cost him dear, he was forced to withdraw from many of the seminary activities. Nor did his caution succeed in forestalling one severe seizure in December, followed at intervals by several minor ones. Unless he improved, he told himself, he would have to forfeit that promised visit to Strasbourg. Therefore he bent his best efforts to the task, circumscribing it as usual to utter conformance with the Divine Will. By the time summer arrived, he was much better.

It was early in August when he set out for Strasbourg. For the first time in long years, three of the brothers Libermann were gathered together; for David visited Samson's house, which now lay just beyond the city at Illkirch, almost daily. His joy at seeing "young Jacob," as he still persisted in calling Francis, was unmitigated. Nine years older, he held not the slightest reverence for the soutane—in fact, he regarded it humorously. On the contrary, Samson held it in great respect —as did also Babette and the children. Lively indeed were the religious discussions between the three brothers; and when Samson and Francis were alone they discussed the fact that David seemed to be passing through the dark valley of unbelief through which they themselves had once wearily plodded. They also discussed the possibility of a visit to Saverne, which seemed to have grown even more difficult now that their half brother Isaac bore the full title and responsibilities of a rabbi. But David reported something which delighted his two brothers.

"A friend of Henoch's, an officer on leave, passed through Saverne when I was there last year. He told us that he had left Henoch studying your Christian New Testament. What on earth is the matter with all of you?" David had continued with a good-natured grin. "Five of the brothers Libermann seem to have taken leave of their senses. I agree that it was a good thing to shed the shackles of the Talmud—but to plunge into something even more absurd, strikes me as a family oddity beyond comprehension."

"Hush, David," whispered Babette, "not in front of the children!"

Little Marie was running toward them across the lawn, her arms flung wide to embrace her godfather, the uncle who wore the soutane. Agnes Léa followed at the more sober gait of ten, her Latin exercise book, in which her uncle was instructing her, tucked tightly under her arm.

Samson questioned Francis at length about his malady, but from out his wide store of medical knowledge he was forced to agree with Dr. Lombard—that science had learned little about the affliction since the days of Hippocrates.

"My dearest brother," Francis said, "do not give yourself concern. Let us regard it as a precious offering to God. If He wishes me cured, He will cure me as no doctor could. If He wishes me to receive the priceless gift of ordination, it will come about in His own time." . . .

The weeks with Samson and his family had sped as on the wings of a skylark. His brief visit to Saverne was far less happy. Between them, the brothers had decided that he could go there in secret, and that his rendezvous with Sarah must be known only to the two. A message had been sent to a trustworthy friend of the family, asking her to arrange the meeting at her home. But when the attractive girl had caught sight of her half brother wearing the despised soutane, she had covered her face with her hands and wept bitterly. With characteristic thoughtfulness Francis had foreseen this eventuality. She was a little older than he had been when he had fled in terror at the sight of the garb—but no doubt it would fill her with the same horror. So he had attempted to change his attire before meeting her; but to his dismay had found the public check room, where he had left his bag, locked up for the time, and he could not make the change.

"It is because I love you so much," the girl sobbed.

He soothed her with gentle words and smiles, and gradually she quieted and listened to him. But his heart was bruised by the violent condemnation she uttered of all he believed. Yet she implored him to remain in Saverne for more than one day, that she might see him once more. He was as reluctant to part, as was she; on the following day they met again by stealth, at an hour when her mother was at the synagogue. They promised to exchange frequent letters, but Francis had to resign himself to the fact that on religious matters they were separated as by an impregnable wall. Now he felt that all he could do would be to carry her tenderly and constantly in his prayers—as he carried David and Henoch.

All the way back to Paris he kept hoping that a letter from Henoch would be awaiting him at the Solitude to confirm David's report. And so to his great joy it befell.

"I can only ask you to forgive my terrible accusation concerning our father," Henoch wrote beseechingly. "And since you are so good a Christian, I know you will forgive. I sinned grievously against you. Since I began to study the New Testament, anguish has been with me night and day. My brother, pray that God will forgive me too. . . . The army has taught me to love Christ. Strange, is it not, that the pursuit of war has led me to the feet of the Prince of Peace? I know how greatly you and Samson, Felkel and Samuel, will rejoice.

Once more we are united as we were when we were small, playing there on the *quai*, romping through the old house, attending synagogue. Only now it is a closer union, although geographically we remain so far apart. But on my next leave I will visit you and Felkel, and Samson. I shall give up soldiering when my term of enlistment expires. Samuel has written, urging me to join him in America."

Francis fell to his knees with tears of thanksgiving. Now there remained only David.

Father Mollevaut was delighted to see the change wrought upon his acolyte by the holiday among his own. And when he heard that no seizure had marred it, and of Henoch's conversion, he exclaimed:

"It's no wonder you look so well! Now that you are back, cling to that restored health and go at your duties sensibly; and let us see if the Solitude will not work a permanent cure."

Francis had scarcely turned his back upon the Superior's office when Le Vavasseur and Tisserant fell upon him, overwhelming in their welcome.

"We thought you would never return!" cried Frederic. "The situation in Bourbon is even more serious; there is much to report."

"We feel sure that now you will think of a way," added Eugene.

Francis regarded the dark, excited young faces with affection.

"We shall have a long talk," he assured them. "It would be well for the world if all the world's missionaries shared your zeal. Shall we meet at the first recreation hour?"

Delightedly the two agreed. Some hours later, after they had painted what indeed was a disturbing picture of Bourbon and Haiti—of Africa—and had read graphic extracts from letters, Francis again counseled patience.

"The time is not yet," he advised them. "God has not yet opened the way. If such a plan is pleasing to Him, it will be made clear to us. Patience, my friends—and prayer!" . . .

But that night when he was alone in his room, he found his heart aching over the plight of God's Negro children the world over, and he gave the matter long and serious consideration—so long and so serious that it would have surprised even Le Vavasseur and Tisserant, had they but known.

Characteristically, and in spite of Father Mollevaut's cautions, Francis soon embarked upon an even more extensive schedule than that of the previous term. His studies absorbed him for many hours of every day. He was virtual director of the enlarged and now extremely popular bands of piety, and devoted spiritual counselor to the souls of many, old and young. His correspondence was now so heavy that frequently he would force himself to rise an hour earlier in order to keep abreast of it. As for the weekly shopping expeditions to Paris, he delighted in them, realizing that thus he was being of service.

Toward the end of the year Father Pinault, who when "in the world" had been a distinguished chemist, replaced Father Mollevaut as Superior. At the start, Francis had puzzled him; he was not sure that he totally approved his methods with the bands of piety. But once having glimpsed the acolyte's basic humility, he discovered in him a soul fundamentally attuned to the religious life. The sympathy and understanding which

soon grew between them were to prove of great consolation
to the two friends throughout the years.

In spite of the exacting schedule Francis passed through
the winter without a seizure. There seemed no doubt of it—
the malady was receding. But in March of 1837, just when he
was beginning timidly to hope, the enemy struck again. And
this time his struggle with a resultant melancholy was more
bitterly fought than in any previous combat. For the long
peace had encouraged him again to dare lift his eyes upward.
Now the dream was irreparably crushed, irretrievably lost.
He tried in vain to see the stars shining through the dark cy-
press trees which guarded the entrance to the Solitude. And
now once more he began to dread the bridges across the
Seine. . . .

It was strange, thought Father Pinault. Libermann had always seemed content to make his excursions into the city
alone, but lately he had been suggesting this or that companion. "I wonder if he fears another seizure?" the Superior had
asked himself. And thereafter he never failed to send a seminarian along with him.

The battle was fought silently—in secret places. No one
knew. No one, that is, save that other suffering One whom he
sought out constantly in chapel. That unfailing Friend de-
vised a means to dispel the gloom. It came suddenly on one
sun-drenched day in May in the shape of a letter from Samson.

"David," he wrote jubilantly, "is won! For all his bravado
and derision last summer when you were here, your talks and
your prayers have had their effect. Shortly after your departure he began to read the Christian literature. But you must

divide honors with the children! Agnes Léa took her uncle in hand as her special project—and little Marie, your godchild, hung a medal of Our Lady about his neck and made him promise not to remove it. (Observe, my brother, that this is the month of May!) Result: He is going to Paris to be baptized, confident that you will arrange it. He wants you to be present; otherwise it could be done here. So you and Felkel must see him through it. Then he plans to take ship for America, upon the urgency of Samuel."

The dark cloud of melancholy which had shrouded the acolyte's soul faded before this glorious shaft of sunshine. Yet another of the brothers Libermann had come into port. And now they were six who had found the peaceful harbor.

Hastening to the city, he first sought out the good friend, Drach; he who had himself once been a rabbi. Drach had steered his own boat into port and would be delighted to do the same for his brother. The smiling and practical Drach at once made all arrangements for David's baptism, securing a priest for the final instructions, and a devout married couple of his acquaintance as godparents. The baptism and First Communion would take place at Stanislas, in the same chapel where they had been bestowed upon Francis.

Then he had hurried across the city to Felkel. The two flung their arms about each other, talking and laughing at once.

"He will arrive in Paris next Monday!" exclaimed Francis.

"And of course he will stay with me!" cried Felkel. . . .

So it was that on the twenty-eighth of May in the year 1837, the little chapel at Stanislas witnessed for the second time the Sacrament of Baptism administered to a Libermann. And of course Drach was again present. Francis, at his side throughout, could scarcely restrain his emotion as he reflected on all this friend had signified in his life. And when David, newborn for all his forty-four years and looking happier than ever before, approached the Communion rail, he made no effort to restrain the tears.

CHAPTER ELEVEN

The Guide

As SUMMER ADVANCED the aura of happiness still clung to Francis. Summer had always been his friend; and this year she was particularly gracious to the Solitude, spreading her green cloak over hillside and valley, setting up a melodious orchestra of many strings in the leafy tree-tops which brushed his small window. He knew that she would protect him from any major seizure. And now that classes were suspended and many were on vacation, he was able to give more time to Le Vavasseur and Tisserant. The two Creoles took their walks with him, dreaming and scheming of the great work upon which they were determined to embark.

They had given the plan a name: *"L'Oeuvre des Noirs,"*— the work for the Negroes. But they could not visualize it without "Father" Libermann at its head. Always he gently brought them back to the point: he was not an ordained priest, and hence could be of little value. Meanwhile, and almost without the two realizing it, he was helping each to seek his own soul's way of perfection. But on those still summer afternoons as the three walked up and down the garden paths of the Solitude, little did they dream that soon they were to be separated. . . .

Off in Brittany in the city of Rennes, more than two hundred miles from Paris, lay the novitiate of Saint-Gabriel, the establishment of the Eudist Fathers. These could look back to the seventeenth century and to Father Eudes, the great apostle of the Sacred Heart of Jesus, for their beginnings. The Revolution had swept away many of their houses and most of their men, but not the spirit which had animated their founder, and which was now rekindling throughout France.

This very summer of 1837 there had journeyed down from Rennes to Paris a certain Abbé Louis, bent on an important mission. The revived Eudist foundation was growing, and now there was a sufficient number of novices to justify full operation of their own novitiate. Heretofore the young men had gone for their training to Saint-Sulpice, whither the errand of the Abbé Louis now carried him. He presented his plea to the Council of the Sulpicians: the Eudists had need of a priest especially fitted to direct young men training for the priesthood—in fine, a director of novices. Would the Council help them find such a man for Rennes?

The Council gave the matter full deliberation. They thought of the bands of piety at Issy. Finally they advised the Abbé Louis:

"We recommend to you the acolyte Libermann. He is not a priest, to be sure. He is only in minor orders. But he is capable of filling the post as well as any priest."

Early on the next day, a hot July morning, Francis had just

left the chapel after making his customary prayer of abandonment to the Divine Will, when a summons from the Superior
reached him.

"How would you like to go to Rennes as director of novices
for the Eudists?" asked Father Pinault.

Francis was speechless with amazement. That anyone
should consider him fit for such a task! And what of leaving
the Solitude where his work was succeeding, where he had
been happy and protected? There was a moment's awkward
pause. Then he heard himself murmur:

"If it should be pleasing to the good God, and to you, Father, I shall gladly go."

In all these years he had been quite unaware that the peace
which had been won from the hardly fought contests—the
long struggle with his malady, the frustration of his hopes for
the priesthood, the endless heartache over his father—had
increasingly made itself manifest. But the Council had not
been unaware of it. When the acolyte had left the room, the
Superior nodded in approval.

"He will do," he murmured to himself.

Francis, alone in his room making preparations for the
journey, told himself that it was not pleasing to his Lord that
he should remain too attached to one place, or to a single
group of friends. After almost five years at the Solitude, he
would miss its peace and beauty, and the eager souls who
turned to him for guidance. But a greater joy than these had
ever held lay in conforming utterly to the Will of his Father
in heaven.

Nevertheless he approached Rennes not without misgiv-
ing. How would the new young men whom he was supposed
to direct regard the supervision of an epileptic—of one who

had been denied the very ordination which they themselves would achieve without great difficulty? How could he acquire an influence over them—particularly after his first public seizure which in the nature of things was bound to come sooner or later? At Issy they had grown accustomed to the seizures and thought little of them. Indeed, it had seemed that they had even won him friends. He recalled the dismay with which these had met the news that he was to be taken from them. Ah well, if it pleased God, they would all meet again. Le Vavasseur and Tisserant had been inconsolable. The work for the Negroes had lost a friend.

At Rennes he would encounter quite a different group. It was however comforting to reflect that some of those from Saint-Sulpice and Issy whom he had counseled would visit Rennes. Some, indeed, planned to make their novitiate there. Francis sighed. He would do the best he could, with the help of the Lord.

Rennes itself, the ancient capital of Brittany where the rivers Ille and Vilaine meet, charmed him. Here again he was to encounter the old Roman roads which as a youth had stirred his thoughts of the mighty civilization which had crumbled in the grasp of its materialistic history. *Urbs Rubra,* the Romans had named it—from the bands of red brick still visible in the foundations of its ancient walls.

The *faubourg* d'Antrain rolled out to the north of the city where stood the novitiate of Saint-Gabriel. Here then Francis was to make his new abode. He arrived early in August of the year 1837. But in spite of his interest in the new work, the change proved difficult for him.

The Abbé Louis, the Eudist Superior, deemed it best that Libermann should begin at Saint-Gabriel as though he himself were a novice, submitting to all the required training, the better to assume later his duties as director of novices. At the same time he looked to Francis to wield a certain spiritual authority, not only over the young men with whom he was sharing a common training, but also over certain already ordained priests desirous of becoming Eudists. It was not an easy role to play. Within himself Francis felt that the novices were not to be blamed if they regarded the situation as anomalous. Here was one who because of a serious malady had never succeeded beyond minor orders—who was older than the youngest by some fifteen years—submitting to the training they themselves were undergoing, yet with no prospect of ever becoming a priest; who was not director of novices and yet to whom they were expected to look for guidance. If they looked in another direction, who could blame them?

In spite of valiant struggles and much prayer, he was unable to throw off the moods of despair which followed every unsuccessful attempt with the novices. To his horror he began to realize that these moods were actually attacks of Satan—a persistent series attempting to destroy his peace with God.

The situation might have remained for some time unchanged but for the visit of Father Lestroan, a Jesuit, who conducted the spiritual retreat which formally opened the fall term. It had not taken him long to evaluate the intellectual and spiritual power of the acolyte who had been trained at Saint-Sulpice and Issy. He sought out the Abbé Louis.

"If you do not make this man director of novices *in fact*, soon," he said, "you will be committing a grievous error. He is a gift from heaven to your struggling novitiate."

A few weeks later, in November, Francis was officially appointed to the post. The difficulties of his former situation began to vanish. With prayer and a vigilance tempered by his innate charity, he was winning the confidence of the novices, one by one. To the troubled and the wavering, he would say:

"Come to see me every day; and whenever you have any difficulty."

His scant leisure time was occupied in a study of the principles which had guided Father Eudes in founding his congregation. He was delighted to discover how closely these approximated the principles laid down by the saintly Father Olier when founding Saint-Sulpice. Both had aimed at training men for a holy priesthood. The Eudists had the additional purpose of an exterior ministry among the faithful and in the missions.

That he might better absorb the spirit of Father Eudes, he spent the cold winter evenings in the community room—one of the few in the house which boasted a fire—seated at a table, busily copying in his rapid handwriting the rules and constitutions and all the writings which the founder had bequeathed to his sons. He let it be understood, however, that all were free to interrupt him for conversation or counsel. The copying was a gigantic work, and over the months totaled more than four hundred pages. Two things came out to him from the finely penned lines: the dedicated spirit of Father Eudes which possessed him increasingly; and the "skeleton and bones" the founder had considered essential in the creation of a religious congregation.

One cold night early in February of 1838, as the retiring bell sounded through the community room and he put away his papers, he was reflecting that the Lord had been very good to him in Rennes. Contrary to his worst fears, there had been no major seizure since his arrival in August. The novices had been spared witnessing an event which would have driven many from him. By now he felt assured that he had won them, and was humbly grateful for the young souls God had put into his hands to mold into the pattern of His priesthood.

Tomorrow would be the vigil of a feast day of great significance to the Eudists—that of the Sacred Heart of Mary. The thought of Mary always touched him most closely when meditating upon her motherhood. As he completed his final prayers and extinguished his candle, he was reflecting on the love with which she must have watched over her Son and cared for Him during the quiet days of Nazareth—before she gave Him up to the indifferent world and to death. . . .

He awoke the next morning tired and depleted from a restless dream. In it he had been a small boy once again, lying in a darkened room, and his mother was placing a cool compress upon his head. It had felt so comforting, quieting his throbbing temples. Then suddenly into the room had strode old Mendelbaum, his teacher—and somehow he knew that the schoolmaster had come to get him. He approached the bed, but Léa had held out her arms to prevent him. Paralyzed with fear, Francis had watched the two struggle there, with Mendelbaum grasping his mother's arm and cruelly bending it behind her. He had wanted to leap from bed to help her, but it was as though his limbs were held in a vice. Then suddenly his father had entered. With stern mien he restrained Léa; and then, turning to the schoolmaster, said: "Take him, and keep him from becoming a priest!" . . .

All the next morning his head had throbbed unbearably. That afternoon there was a general assemblage of teachers and students called together to hear the plans for tomorrow's feast day. Francis was sitting quietly with the novitiate professors when suddenly he heard the voice of the Abbé Louis calling him to the rostrum.

"The Director of Novices will speak to us on the significance of the great feast day we shall observe tomorrow," he was saying.

The summons had come without warning. In a panic, Francis wondered what he would say. He had made no preparation. Obediently he arose, trying to subdue the sudden trembling of his knees. An unbearable quiet had fallen upon the room. Standing before them all, he began bravely enough. But scarcely had he uttered the first sentence when the long quiescent enemy, rising in sudden and unleashed fury, struck him down there before their horrified gaze. He writhed on the floor, his body beaten and belabored by blows from the unseen force—the fine mouth covered with a bloody foam, the eyes rolled upward into their sockets. It was the worst seizure he had ever experienced. And in all its horror, his novices witnessed it. Three-quarters of an hour passed before the tormented form lay quiet. . . .

The older priests with their gentle faces crept in quietly, one by one, to see him in the infirmary. To their surprise, they found him completely at peace, with no trace of depression or self-pity—his spirit serene. The Abbé Louis came also, but for all his sympathy was unable to conceal his disappointment. With the Council of Saint-Sulpice he had shared the hope that the change to Rennes might effect a permanent cure—and that Francis would achieve to ordination there. Now, one could no longer hope.

At length one day there came a timid young novice—one

who had devotedly followed Francis from the start. The patient greeted him with a winning smile and held out his hand.

"Behold, my dear young friend, how worthless a creature you have as a director of novices," he said.

The youth turned aside to hide the tears which sprang to his eyes. . . .

When Francis was up and about again, with vision only too clear he recognized that the hold he had achieved upon the novices through months of effort had now been irrevocably broken. Had his Lord abandoned him, then? He could not believe that—and yet, whence sprang this great desolation of soul? He regarded himself as the most useless of all human creatures—beyond the contempt of God and man.

February folded into March, and March into April—and still the inner desolation, suspected by no one, did not lessen. Many of the novices avoided him; others gave him only a perfunctory courtesy. Even the advent of summer, his good companion, could not succeed in lifting up his heart. But at length there came a respite. For on one burnished July day he was told that Frederic Le Vavasseur, on holiday, had arrived from Paris. The Creole of Bourbon had journeyed to Rennes expressly to see "Father" Libermann about the work for the Negroes.

Francis rejoiced greatly upon meeting his friend again, and hearing all the news of his beloved Solitude. Together the two held long discussions. Interest in the cause of the Negroes was growing at the seminary of Issy, Frederic told him, and many had expressed a desire to join the movement. But they looked to Libermann in Rennes to lead it. For a time, Francis gave himself up to the idea that if such a group of missionary priests were to be formed, they could not do better than to affix themselves to the Eudist foundation which included missions in its general plan. His own part in the undertaking remained a matter of great doubt. He must wait, he told Frederic, until God would signify what He wished of him. Meantime, he would help them all he could.

When Le Vavasseur returned to Issy at the start of the fall term, he found Tisserant among the many new devotees of the old Paris church which had experienced an extraordinary revival of faith—Notre-Dame-des-Victoires. There the pastor, Abbé Desgenettes, despairing of awakening any devotion in what then was a godless parish in the heart of the city, had been on the point of abandoning his charge when one day on the altar, his heart breaking in discouragement, he had heard the whispered words: "Consecrate thy church and thy parish to the Most Holy and Immaculate Heart of Mary."

He lost no time in doing so, and from then on there occurred a revival of faith in the neighborhood which was nothing short of miraculous. The hitherto almost empty church was now full of worshippers from early morning until nightfall, drawn by the sanctity of the Abbé, his eloquent preaching, and the devotion to Mary, who seemed to smile there upon the petitions of the weary and the oppressed. Soon it seemed that all of Paris was finding its way to the doors of Notre-Dame-des-Victoires. The Abbé assembled them all into a great confraternity dedicated to the Immaculate Heart. Young Tisserant from Haiti, the devout seminarian, had been among the first to join.

Le Vavasseur followed him, and the two now carried their petitions for *L'Oeuvre des Noirs* to Our Lady in her especially favored church. They also talked at length with the Abbé Desgenettes. It so fell out that on February 2, 1839, they were among the throng listening to him preach. To their joy, they heard him launch upon the subject of the abandoned Negroes, and implore his congregation to pray that the work of their salvation might go forward. And so it seemed to do from that hour.

But Francis, who remained at Rennes in great desolation of spirit, had received no interior signal that such was to be his work. It seemed to him that it had been amply shown that he did not belong in a seminary, and he began to dream of a solitary life of prayer and meditation. There were times when he felt certain that death approached, and when he longed for it with all his heart. He would spend the brief, intervening time totally withdrawn from the world. . . .

But these were only dreams. Actually, he had no will save that of his Master. "My Jesus," he would pray, "Thou knowest well that I am nothing, am capable of nothing, am worth nothing. Behold me as I am! In Thy great mercy, take me if it be agreeable to Thee. I abandon, I deliver myself into Thy hands; I desire nought besides. Will for me, and in me. . . . If sometimes I resist Thee, pay no attention, my good Master. It is not I who wish to withstand Thy love, but this wretched flesh of mine. I renounce it, and will to renounce it, for ever and ever."

Meantime Le Vavasseur was writing from Issy:

"The work is growing. Many here now would join us. Do you remember De la Brunière? He is pledged to go along with us, and cannot wait to start."

Yes, Francis remembered De la Brunière as a devoted member of the bands of piety. The acolyte's ever-present practical sense told him that De la Brunière would be a great

asset to the plan. A member of a distinguished family, a
nephew of the Bishop of Mende and heir to a fortune, he also
possessed many talents. Above all, he had the spirit of devotion and sacrifice. It was well indeed that De la Brunière had
aligned himself with the work for the Negroes.

He wrote to Le Vavasseur, advising frequent counsel with
his good friend, Father Pinault, who remained the Superior at
the Solitude. There, it was Father Pinault, and Le Vavasseur's
confessor, Father Gallais, who were advising the leaders of
the embryo society. Francis, from Rennes, was himself in frequent correspondence with Pinault. The two found themselves in complete agreement upon the matter. The new society must be composed of highly dedicated souls who would
live together in community and abide by austere rules and
constitutions. Each should be ready and eager to carry the
message of Christ to the farthermost corners of the earth—
and, if need be, to die for it.

At about this time his enthusiastic young Creole friends
began pressing Francis to draw up a set of rules and constitutions for the proposed society. But he held back. It seemed
to him that many other matters must be settled first. Apart
from long spiritual preparation and prayer, there was Rome
—without whose approval no new missionary congregation
could be launched. Someone would eventually have to go to
Rome. . . .

When the vacation period began in the summer of 1839,
Father Pinault having written that the Solitude would welcome him, Francis journeyed to Paris and the seminary at
Issy. For long he had been yearning to talk with the Superior;
with that delightful Greek scholar, Father Mollevaut; with

his early and much-loved advisers, the Abbé Augé, Father
Faillon, and Father Carbon. This surely would help to restore
his spirit and perhaps to give direction to his present flounder-
ing and uncharted course.

The visit brought its consolations. Particularly enlighten-
ing had been his discussions with Pinault concerning the
work for the Negroes. But he returned to Rennes no more
certain of his future course than when he had left.

At Issy he had talked with some of the new recruits to the
work, and had been impressed again by the fervor and ability
of De la Brunière, whom many now thought should assume
the leadership of the movement. It had been arranged that
De la Brunière would visit Rennes in the fall, when he would
have finished his theological studies. There he hoped to persuade "Father" Libermann to draw up the rules and constitutions. The others at Issy counted on the enthusiasm of the
young seminarian to win Francis totally to the work. . . .

It was late in September when the emissary arrived at the
Eudist novitiate. But he found that Francis still hesitated to
formulate the rules, convinced that they should be of a severity compatible with the selfless purposes of such a ministry, and fearing lest the austerity he envisioned as essential
would discourage the young souls who were drawn to it. As
for any deeper personal involvement in the plans, he still
waited in darkness for some affirmative signal from his Master. His arrested status in the religious life appeared to the
acolyte to be a permanent barrier. He viewed his case as
hopeless.

Late in October on the eve of the Feast of St. Simon and St.
Jude, De la Brunière asked him to offer Holy Communion the

next morning for their plan. The powerful friend of the hopeless, St. Jude, did not fail them. For as the acolyte was attending with great devotion, suddenly the veil was lifted. He knew at once that he must concern himself vitally with this work—although to what extent was not yet revealed. And with the light, there came a great upsurge of the spirit. He could write encouragingly to Le Vavasseur, and he promised to reflect deeply upon the rules and constitutions. At the same time he sent a letter to Father Pinault, to whom he opened his soul. The reply he received seemed to stamp his vocation with certitude.

Swiftly the plans were made with the delighted De la Brunière. Together they would journey to Rome to seek the Holy Father's approval of the proposed society. Francis would go by way of Paris, and his companion, who would finance the trip, would meet him in Marseilles, whence they would sail for Rome. Francis would leave Rennes on December 2, 1839. There remained only the matter of breaking the news to the Abbé Louis. And this proved one of the most difficult tasks Francis had ever undertaken. For although his uncertain situation with the Eudists was fraught with the difficulties and frustrations which stemmed from his malady, and although he was bound by no promise to remain, he yet could not rid himself of the feeling that he was deserting them. This plunged him into a deep melancholy.

He had really wanted to be of service to the Eudists. But ruefully he told himself that in November of 1839 he seemed not much more advanced toward that goal than he had been on the day he had arrived two years before. In any case, he now had no choice. It had at length been made abundantly clear what he must do. He must proceed with the work even without having achieved ordination—even as a humble acolyte.

How to tell the Abbé Louis? In spite of Francis' uncertain health, the Superior had seemed to value the many practical services which he rendered daily. In all humility, Francis recognized that his departure would create a problem. It seemed to him that a letter which would present in orderly fashion all his reasons, and also his sincere devotion to the Eudists, would be the best method. And so, three days before his departure, and although the two were under the same roof, he wrote to the Abbé.

His nature was such that it had ever caused him pain to inflict the slightest disappointment upon others. Ah well, he thought, as he unhappily awaited in his bare little room the Superior's reply, he would survive this present pain. If he had been able to live through his agonies caused by the blow he had dealt his father, he should be able to survive the suffering attendant upon the disappointments he might cause any others! Except One—that One, he must never disappoint, and His wishes now seemed clear to him. Surely the good Abbé Louis would understand. He knew the dire need of the Negroes, and would bless the new undertaking with all his heart.

Just then a rap sounded on his door. He jumped up, thinking it was a novice bearing the Superior's reply. But to his surprise it was the Abbé himself—and looking sterner than Francis had ever seen him. He entered quietly and closed the door. For a moment there was silence in the small room as the two looked at each other. Then the Superior of the Eudist foundation spoke.

"Your plan," he declared severely, "can be prompted only by self-love. I regard it as a diabolical invention of the Evil One himself!"

Francis paled and clutched the back of his solitary chair for support.

CHAPTER TWELVE

The Father

THE NEPHEW OF the Bishop of Mende, young
Paul de la Brunière, looked about him with distaste and drew
his warm cloak closer. So this was the *pensionnat de famille*
to which they had been recommended by their friends in
Paris! Was there nothing better for visiting French clergy in
all the city of Rome?

Outside a cold, dismal rain was falling on this early January
day of the year 1840—the Feast of the Epiphany. It beat a
nervous tattoo against the grimy windows, and was flooding
the near-by Forum of Trajan, as he and Francis, their clothing drenched, followed the host up a stairway whose carpet
was worn threadbare, and into the two sad, adjoining rooms
which had been assigned to them.

Francis was already setting down his shabby portmanteau,
and with one of his sunniest smiles was assuring Signor Jourdan, who spoke a rapid if incorrect French, that their accom-
modations were perfect. "How can he smile," wondered Paul,
"when the scene is so desolate?"

Paul de la Brunière—he had now received the subdeacon-ship—had not missed the quick appraising eye their host had cast upon his companion's attire. Poor Libermann! That cloak was almost in shreds. He must cast about tomorrow for an excuse to present him with a new one. It would never do to have him appear before cardinals, perhaps even the Holy Father himself, clothed as he was. It would be risking the great cause itself. The cloak had looked bad enough when they had taken ship from Marseilles. But now, after six days of a rough sea voyage, plus the downpour with which Italy had greeted them, it was fit only for the rubbish heap.

The two travelers were extremely weary; but the destination so long desired having at last been achieved, each found himself too stimulated to retire early. After a simple meal shared in common with their host and his family—for at the moment they were the only guests—they found their way into a small parlor on the ground floor where a little brazier of coals was struggling unsuccessfully against the damp chill of the winter evening.

"Since we met in Marseilles a week ago," observed De la Brunière, "we have talked so constantly about your conferences in Paris that I have neglected to ask about your departure from Rennes. I thought about it all the time I was visiting my family, and hoped you had accomplished it without difficulty."

The truth was that Francis had been skillfully avoiding the subject, fearing that if he spoke of it he might betray himself into a lapse of charity. Despite valiant efforts he had not been able to conquer his wounded feelings, nor untangle them from the shock and dismay of the experience. But now, under the sympathetic questioning of a friend, and in his fatigue, he succumbed to the human urge to pour forth the whole story. After all, they two would now be working closely together, and it was best that his companion should know all his weaknesses, know how far he remained from being the saintly leader they all imagined him to be.

He meant to choose his words carefully, to keep well in the forefront of his mind his very real affection for the Abbé Louis. But as he began to speak, his normal constraint deserted him, and De la Brunière surprisingly found himself listening to the unrestrained cry of a hurt and outraged soul.

That the Abbé Louis should call their great aim of saving the poor Negroes a snare of the Evil One! That he should accuse him, Francis—the poor acolyte who knew better than anyone his own unworthiness for the priesthood—of acting through self-love! That he should have poured down abuse upon him; that he should have tried every means to keep him at Rennes; and finally, when he saw that he could not succeed, that he should have exacted a promise that Francis would consult several important ecclesiastics on the wisdom of this step before leaving France—and last but not least, that the Abbé Louis should have advised him to ignore the encouraging counsel of their own wise and holy Father Pinault!

"He tried his best to induce me to write you that I had given up the whole idea, that I would not meet you. You can imagine, my dear Paul, what this did to me. I was attacked again fiercely by headaches. I feared another seizure was imminent. My soul was torn with doubts and apprehensions; and you could never guess the great desolation of spirit which he relentlessly brought upon me."

De la Brunière looked at his companion curiously. Surely, this was a new Libermann, one he had never met before.

Francis, gazing into the flickering coals, seemed to have forgotten him and to be talking aloud with his own soul.

"Deliberately I chose the feast of St. Francis Xavier, the great Jesuit missionary, which fell just three days later, for my departure. But all the way to Paris I suffered—wondering indeed whether I had been mistaken in interpreting the will of our Beloved Master. And even there among our friends, so full of enthusiasm for the cause—those who look to us to accomplish so much for it here—even when with our spiritual leader, Father Pinault, who encouraged us and gave assurances that he would do everything possible for the work, even when in the midst of all that trust and confidence, I could not shake off a sense of doubt and guilt about the whole matter. The Abbé Louis' contempt had seared my soul. And I felt that God had deserted me."

"And did you in fact consult other ecclesiastics, as you had promised him?" inquired De la Brunière.

"Oh, yes! And what did I meet? Saving two, precisely the same attitude as that of the Superior of Rennes. They all advised me to turn back. There were some in Lyons who roundly insulted me. Having been recommended to the Superior of a certain religious community there, I went to him and begged his counsel. He received me coldly and did not even ask me to sit down, standing himself as I recited the story. When I had finished, he suddenly burst into roars of laughter, turned abruptly and left the room without even a word of farewell."

De la Brunière was thinking: "Why, there's actual bitterness in his tone. I never noticed that before."

"And finally," Francis was continuing rapidly, his face flushed, its customary serene peace disturbed as when a sudden squall strikes at a still lake, "finally came the greatest insult. One morning, wishing to perform my duties as acolyte and to serve at Holy Mass, I presented myself at a certain rectory door. There a priest answered my request by looking me up and down as though I were so much filth. 'The state of your clothing,' he said, 'prohibits such a privilege.' And with that he shut the door in my face."

His companion stirred uneasily. A long moment passed before he replied. When he did so, there was a note of strain in his voice.

"I'm sorry," he said, "very, very sorry. You have indeed met with most unfortunate experiences. But tonight you are tired. Come! Let us off to bed. Tomorrow the skies will seem brighter for both of us."

But when he reached his room, De la Brunière found that he could not sleep. He paced up and down, and finally dug into his portmanteau for some sheets of letter paper. Ink and a pen were on a little table. Impulsively he sat down and scrawled off a half-dozen rapid pages to Father Pinault. On the night of their arrival in Rome, he confessed to utter discouragement. In such hands as it now rested, the plan would never progress. Between the lines there crept his disillusionment concerning the "saint" he thought he had been following.

Meanwhile Francis, in his own room, was on his knees before his crucifix, the tears blinding him.

"Forgive, O great Pardoner. For one awful hour I have been guilty of betraying You. The Abbé Louis is right. I am devoured by self-love, self-pity. Purge me of it, O great Pardoner, who didst stoop to wash the feet of Your disciples!"

True to his companion's prophecy, the next morning smiled upon Rome and upon the two pilgrims. In spite of his letter written the night before, De la Brunière awoke with the determination to buy the new cloak for Francis. It was only a common charity—whether he remained with him or not. And he was not at all sure that he would remain. If the Jewish acolyte had been received so poorly all along the way, how much more poorly would he be received here! Here sat all the might and dignity of the Church—purple, and red, red merging into a white so pure and spotless as to dazzle the eyes.

After an early morning Mass at St. Peter's, at which Francis seemed to be totally lifted out of himself, Paul quietly went off to buy the cloak, leaving his friend wrapped in prayer at the tomb of the great Apostle.

By coincidence, an hour later the two converged within a block of their lodging. Paul was forced to smile as he beheld a totally different Francis than the one who had talked into the fire the night before. Libermann's very step seemed lighter. His fine head was thrown back, and on his face once again there rested that singular peace. As they fell into step together, Francis said:

"To think I am here because of your generosity! My friend, I am very grateful. To have seen St. Peter's! To have received the Sacrament there; to have prayed at the tomb of the greatest, the first missionary! I have asked for every blessing upon you, and upon our difficult task. But here's a strange thing. My prayers were suddenly, compellingly interrupted by the thought of Drach. You know, he managed my baptism, and that of my brother David. Now I cannot but feel that he is going to play a part in this, also."

"Did you see him when you were in Paris?"

"No, more's the pity. When I had finished all the conferences at the Solitude—Pinault, Le Vavasseur, Tisserant, and

all the rest—there was no time. There was scarcely time to
see my brother Felkel. But today I shall write him and outline
our plans."

As Libermann and De la Brunière entered their hostelry,
they were told that a gentleman waited to see them. Considerably mystified, they drew aside the heavy portiere of the
small parlor. A tall figure rose to greet them. His back was to
the light, and it took Francis a full minute to recognize him.
Then with a joyous cry he sprang forward and embraced the
smiling visitor.

"Drach!" he cried. "From where have you dropped?"

"There, there, Francis," said the other, beaming, "you might
leave some breath in me to greet your companion."

"Paul, this is the friend about whom I was just speaking,
Monsieur Drach. And this is my colleague, Paul de le Brunière."

Happily the three sat down as Drach explained his presence in Rome.

"I've been here for some weeks," he said, "having unex-
pectedly received the honor of appointment as Librarian to
the Office of the Propaganda."

Francis could not contain his joy.

"But no one in Paris told me!"

"Father Pinault thought you would enjoy the surprise," explained Drach. "He himself has had the experience of being a
stranger in great cities, and knows what it means unexpect-
edly to encounter an old friend."

"And has he told you," urged Francis, "why we are here?"

"All of that; in the same letter apprising me when and
where I would find you."

Rapidly they launched upon a full discussion of their project. Drach's knowledge of Rome, of protocol, and of personalities, filled the two visitors with a new confidence. He advised them of the calls they must first make, approved of the plan that Francis should start writing a tentative program of rule for the proposed society—and said finally:

"Of course you must have an audience with the Pope."

"But—can that be arranged?" asked Francis dubiously.

Drach smiled. "It will be arranged," he said firmly. "Probably early next month would be the best time. By then you will have acquired a little Italian; your plans will be better organized, and part of your provisional rule may be down on paper."

He did not leave them before getting their promise to meet him that evening for dinner as his guests, at a certain restaurant in an ancient building which had been an inn in the days of St. Ignatius.

Libermann was so overjoyed that he cleared the worn stairs in no time, with De la Brunière a close second. Throwing open his door, he paused in surprise at the sight of a package which had been laid upon his bed.

"It must be for someone else," he said, bending over to scan the address.

"No, it's for you," said Paul. "A gift, to wish you Godspeed in Rome." . . .

Never had Francis been as busy as during the next few weeks. Here in the city whose civilization had produced the old roads which had fascinated him in Alsace, in France; which had left its mark upon far-away Saverne, upon Metz, and upon Rennes, he had to turn his back resolutely upon sight-seeing. Between an exacting schedule of religious devotions; pilgrimages to the great basilicas; appointments with church dignitaries whom Drach wished him to consult; and many hours alone in his room working on the rule—how he blessed the saintly Father Eudes whose program he had studied with such concentration—as well as regular reports to Paris, he had little time to observe an increasing reticence on the part of De la Brunière.

Once or twice it had occurred to him that Paul had seemed unduly depressed; but he had put it down to the urgency his friend felt to start off for the missions immediately. He knew that he chafed at the delay, at the amount of red tape which must be cut through before the new society could be launched —if, indeed, it could ever be launched. He sighed as he reflected on the coolness and indifference with which many churchmen had greeted their proposal. But as long as Drach had confidence, as long as Father Pinault wrote encouragingly, as long as Le Vavasseur and Tisserant and the other young zealots sent hopeful letters, he would not give way to discouragement. . . . And he tried his best to cheer De la Brunière.

The more he thought about their project, the wiser it seemed to propose first, not the immediate foundation of a new congregation, but to begin by asking permission to form a sort of auxiliary unit of priests with mission vocations who would go anywhere the Holy See might desire, and who would live under a simple community rule. This modest door should be easier to enter. But always he left the decision to the Master of all missionaries—and waited in prayer and silence for the answer.

At length dawned the day of the audience with the Holy Father, carefully arranged by Drach who was to accompany them. As Francis dressed himself with more care than usual on that morning of the seventeenth of February, 1840, he turned over in his mind, not so much the project of which he hoped to speak, but the assurance, the comfort, which lay in the very words, "Holy Father." How beautiful was the name "Father"! First, and above all, was the "Father of Lights in whom there is no change nor shadow of alteration"; then, the Holy Father, guarding the heritage of his children everywhere—watching over them, protecting them. Then came the memory, with full force, of his earthly father—never without its pain of love.

All that the good Rabbi had been to him when he was a child and a youth was but a reflection of the perfection of fatherhood which he had only come to understand, with his limited, human understanding, when within the Catholic Church. With a smile and a pang he recalled his father's sternness coupled with the loving solicitude; the harsh rule and the sudden and unexpected gentleness; the wide generosity. He remembered as though it were yesterday, the touch of his hand—how it had felt when laid upon his head, imparting an unutterable kindness. . . . He had learned to close a door in his mind on the later years; on the beloved one's death, by turning instantly to prayer. Beware of that door! Behind it lay the unconquerable sorrow. And also, or so he had come to suspect, the spring that set off the headaches, the trembling—and even the seizures themselves. . . . It had been two years now, since the enemy had attacked.

Francis, on his knees in the great chamber in which Pope Gregory XVI was to receive them, tried to still the beating of his heart. At last he was to meet, face to face, his other earthly father. Drach, kneeling at his side, smiled encouragement. Paul at his left, was obviously nervous, his folded hands twitching. But with the entrance of the serene white figure, a great peace and calm seemed to enfold them.

The Holy Father repeated the names as Drach gave them: "the Abbé Libermann" (Francis wondered wildly if he should interrupt and cry out: "But I've not been ordained!") and "the Abbé de la Brunière." The Pope's voice had a certain high, sweet quality—almost like that of a child, Francis thought. Lovingly the Pontiff bent over them, and placed his hand on the Jewish acolyte's head, allowing it to remain there for a long moment. Drach thought he saw a fleeting light pass across the Holy Father's face. And something that had been long asleep, stirred deeply, happily, within the soul of Francis.

Drach was speaking; was telling the Pope about the plan to aid the salvation of God's Negro children in the world's abandoned places. The Holy Father smiled with pleasure and turned again to Francis, bidding him persevere and blessing him. It seemed as though he were about to say more, when suddenly a figure loomed hesitantly in the doorway—that of a cardinal, crimson-robed, bent on an errand of state. Reluctantly the two younger men, deeply moved, withdrew, as with a gesture the Holy Father detained Drach.

"Tell me," he said softly, in a voice which showed emotion, "who is he whose head I have just touched?"

The Librarian of the Propaganda outlined briefly the history of the convert from Saverne. The Pope listened with thoughtful eyes. When Drach had finished, he spoke.

"*Questo sara un Santo!*" exclaimed Pope Gregory XVI. "That one will become a saint!" . . .

At the time, the Librarian of the Propaganda confided this episode solely to his diary. . . .

For the next few days Francis walked about in a state of exaltation. Having lost an earthly father, he had found one. No matter, if the plan dragged slowly; no matter if De la Brunière seemed increasingly discouraged. His Holy Father had told him to persevere—and he would, to the end. And so the innumerable interviews continued, until finally in early March he was presented to Monsignor Cadolini, Secretary of the Propaganda, who gave him permission to present a memorandum outlining the project.

Francis drew up a carefully worded petition, in which he submitted himself and the group entirely to the wishes of the Propaganda. The document was a model of forthrightness. While presenting a strong case for the aspirants, it omitted nothing unfavorable—their youth, the fact that most of them were still students—and frankly stated the case of their representative in Rome who confessed to being much older than the others, but yet not promoted to Holy Orders because of "a disease which, during nine years has gradually decreased." Francis stated that, if it were no obstacle to his mission, he would prefer to remain all his life in minor orders.

He was told to return in eight days for a reply. An unaccountable depression fell upon the two who waited at the Jourdan hostelry for those eight days to pass. Paul took to making long pilgrimages of prayer to his favorite basilica, Santa Maria Maggiore; but Francis could not escape the impression that he was avoiding him. At length came the time to return to the Propaganda for a reply. It was a cold, blustery March day, and the petitioner was grateful for the warm cloak his friend had given him. But his steps slowed increasingly as he neared Monsignor Cadolini's office, and his heart was heavy with a sense of impending defeat.

It was not unwarranted. Monsignor Cadolini told him explicitly that before expecting any decision from the Propaganda on such a proposal, he must first become a priest. Francis felt as though cold water had suddenly been thrown into his face. It was like saying to a man born blind: "Before I can help you, you must be able to see." He was too shaken to explain to the Secretary all the circumstances which had persistently barred him from the priesthood, and the reluctance of doctors to pronounce any epileptic permanently cured. With a few polite phrases he bowed himself out. His memorandum remained on Monsignor Cadolini's desk. He had forgotten that it did not bear his address.

But as he made his way homeward in bewilderment and disappointment, his first thought was, characteristically, not of himself but of others. Paul! This would be a blow to him. And to Le Vavasseur and Tisserant, eagerly waiting in Paris for some good news; and to all the others only counting the days until they could join the new society. He would not give up their cause. The Holy Father had told him to persevere—and persevere he would. Yet now his steps lagged even more than they had when approaching the Propaganda. His distaste at bringing disappointment to anyone made it difficult to bear the equivocal answer to De la Brunière.

They spent a miserable evening together; De la Brunière, silent and morose, and Francis feeling wretchedly culpable. Everything was his fault! What insane vanity had ever possessed him to succumb to their immature pleadings to lead the movement? Those young men had been mistaken, but his own error was the worse. Suddenly the temples began to set up their excessive throbbing. He excused himself and retired, knowing that only rest—and prayer in solitude—could forestall a seizure. But if it were God's will that it should come, he would gladly accept it. . . . All the next day he remained shut up in his room.

When he emerged at nightfall, Paul was waiting for him, looking nervous and shamefaced.

"I'm going back to Paris," he blurted out, flushing to the roots of his hair.

They had been standing in the small parlor, waiting for supper to be announced. Francis reached for a chair and sat down suddenly.

"But Paul—we are not defeated yet. We have not tried half the avenues. We have not even had time to consult Monsieur Drach on this new development. I'm sure he will suggest means of reaching Monsignor Cadolini's ear again. After all, the Secretary does not know the complete story—nor how impossible his directive is."

"I'm going back to Paris," repeated the other stubbornly. "Although I've said nothing to you about it, I've been thinking of it for a long time."

"I know," said Francis gently. "But you are too quickly discouraged. If only easy things should be undertaken, what would become of the Church? St. Peter and St. John would have continued to fish in the Lake of Tiberias; and St. Paul would never have left Jerusalem."

"Nothing you can say will dissuade me. My mind is made up. Believe me, Francis, I'm sorry to leave you. Perhaps one of the others will come to replace me—"

"Then you no longer wish to be a missionary?"

"On the contrary. I desire it more than all else in the world. And now I believe that prayer has revealed that such must certainly be my life."

"Then why not wait a little with me?"

"It's not a question of waiting a little. I'm sorry to say it, Francis, but I have no hope you can succeed. You know your barrier to the priesthood better than I. And since you have said that you will not try that door again—that you prefer to remain always in minor orders—I have no other choice."

"But what will you do in Paris?"

"I shall apply at once for admission into the Seminary of the Foreign Missions—and beg for a speedy assignment in China."

Within twenty-four hours the two friends had parted—not without sorrow on De la Brunière's part and a secret, gnawing sense of guilt; and on Libermann's part, a feeling of desolation and betrayal. Alone in his room, he counted out the money his friend had left with him. It would not suffice for food and lodging for more than a fortnight. Not without bitterness did he recall Paul's last words:

"Just as soon as you are ready to return to Paris—and the sooner you make that decision the better—let me know and I will defray the traveling expenses."

Apparently his colleague had decided that he should not remain in Rome longer than two weeks. Yet had the Holy Father told him to persevere. . . .

As the first dismal, lonely day passed without his companion, Francis realized that the letters he had sent to Father Pinault, to Le Vavasseur and Tisserant, announcing the first major setback would scarcely have reached Paris before the arrival of De la Brunière. He shrank from thinking of the pessimistic picture that Paul would paint. He pitied the young zealots, burning with the missioners' vocation. Would they lose all faith in him now—just when his will had become more firmly set than ever to accomplish their design? Just when he was determined, as never before, to persevere? Suddenly his despair knew no bounds. He buried his head in his hands, and wept.

Prayer sustained him through the long days of waiting for return letters from Paris. At length they came. To his joy, he was urged to continue his efforts—the aspirants still had faith in him. They remained untroubled by De la Brunière's defection—even though it had created a financial problem. But they would get money to him somehow—although most of them had little enough of it. Francis began looking about at once for less expensive quarters. It might be a long siege. He would gladly go hungry, if need be—but he would not give up.

The house of the Patriarca family stood on a narrow road, graced by no footpaths, but rather bisected by a gutter in which floated the noisome debris of the entire crowded and lively neighborhood. The poorest of the visiting clergy found their way to its door. Of its kindly and voluble master, Francis begged to be allowed to rent the cheapest of his lodgings. It turned out to be an attic with sloping eaves, under most of which it was impossible to stand upright, and in which nested a colony of pigeons. For furniture, there was a small table, two chairs, an iron washstand, and a mattress laid on the stone floor. The brighter aspect proved to be an outside stairway, with a little balcony on the landing outside his door.

The discomfort mattered little, as long as he could serve at an early Mass every day, and make his customary devotions. A bit of bread and black coffee sufficed for his breakfast; he partook of a meal at one o'clock with the Patriarca family —and for supper he shared what was left of the dry bread with the pigeons who now regarded him as their great friend. He who had been the best commissionaire that the Solitude had ever known, could keep himself alive at small expense and yet have something left over to share.

After some days had passed, De la Brunière, regretting the manner of his withdrawal, began to send small sums from time to time. Although they were not really sufficient to maintain him, Francis managed. Soon his erstwhile companion, now ordained, wrote happily that his dream had been fulfilled. The Seminary of Foreign Missions had found an assignment for him in China. He was to leave immediately, and would labor in Manchuria. He was now a full-fledged missionary.

Francis pondered and prayed unceasingly over the next step for his own "missionaries." He consulted constantly with Drach, but knew in his heart that he must wait for his Master to show him the path. There was yet another matter upon which his prayers went up constantly for direction. After much reflection, Father Pinault had written that he now felt sure that the acolyte must again seek ordination to the priesthood. More than two years having passed since the last seizure, his friend believed him to be cured. Rome was right. He could do the cause little good until he had become a priest. . . . That, thought Francis, was all in the hands of God. As for himself, he yet was convinced of his total unworthiness.

April and May blossomed over Rome—and the little worktable under the eaves bore on its sturdy surface a prodigious amount of labor. Rapidly the pen moved, building the provisional rule of the proposed society. The building had gone slowly until one day he had made a special pilgrimage to all the well-known sanctuaries of Our Lady in the city, praying as he had prayed at Notre-Dame-des-Victoires. As he was returning to his humble loft, he suddenly knew that the society must be dedicated to the Most Holy Heart of Mary. From that moment, the work went smoothly.

Daily correspondence was intensive, his spiritual petitioners having traced him to Rome. And now his replies seemed to carry even more solace and depth than formerly. . . . "We do not live for ourselves, nor should we live in ourselves —or by ourselves," he wrote to a troubled seminarian. "Simply determine that you are going to keep yourself in the presence of God—and that is all."

Of course Samson and Babette in Strasbourg were not neglected; and Samson was jubilant over the long surcease from the malady. "We may now hope," he wrote, "that the affliction has passed—thanks to the great mercy of God. We only await your ordination. . . ." Francis was not so sure. Although the epilepsy was quiescent, the headaches recurred frequently; and there had been distressing attacks of Roman fever.

Of late he had been studying the Gospel of St. John again, verse by verse, chapter by chapter, and as only few students could—in an early Hebrew version, in truth in his mother tongue. It had brought him boundless peace and beauty; and now he began to write down his own reflections upon it. The world praises the power of forceful men—but John, through gentleness, had done more for mankind than any forceful man in history. "Having loved His own who were in the world, He loved them unto the end." How many a weary soul, perhaps tempted toward self-destruction—Francis knew at least one such—had listened to those words, and felt his heart lifted up within him? . . . "My little children, love one another," had been John's total and perpetual sermon to his flock, in the later years. Love was the simple key to everything. How well John had understood it; had helped others to understand it!

Meanwhile, although it had seemed to Francis and those waiting in Paris that the door of the Office of the Propaganda had swung shut upon their cherished project, that bureau had been carefully examining the memorandum left upon Monsignor Cadolini's desk. Inquiries had been sent to Paris, and all the replies being favorable, Cardinal Fransoni, Prefect of the Congregation, one day in early June sat down to write a letter of encouragement to the group's representative in Rome—that oddly arresting Jew who was only half a priest. His name was affixed to the document—Francis Marie Paul Libermann—but where under the sun was his address? With some difficulty, the Cardinal obtained it.

The next day in his little garret, Francis was startled to receive an important-looking letter bearing the impressive seal of the Propaganda. With unsteady hands and with the pigeons fluttering about him, he read that his proposal had been received at a time which seemed most propitious for the propagation of the faith. "Although the Sacred Congregation has resolved to examine this matter more maturely, and to reserve its approbation for another time, yet it thought well to exhort you and your associates to persevere in your design, and to neglect nothing to correspond with your vocation."

That paragraph alone sent more joy into the petitioner's heart than he had known for a long time. But the next paragraph left him breathless and with mingled emotions. "The Sacred Congregation is confident that God, who is most bountiful and all powerful, will give you sufficient health to receive Holy Orders, and to devote yourself entirely with your fellow laborers to the sacred ministry." . . .

Ah, the Cardinal did not know the long, secret story—the years of striving, of ardent hopes, and the sudden and awful frustrations. Had not these been sufficient to indicate that his Saviour desired of him a more humble role? For the time he would think no more on that paragraph—but would write joyously at once to the small, discouraged group in Paris.

His letter crossed an equally joyous one from Le Vavasseur. A Benedictine missionary had appeared in Paris, Bishop Collier, vicar apostolic of the island of Mauritius, who sought missionaries for work among the Negroes of his diocese. He would gladly absorb the whole group—and, best of all, he would confer Holy Orders upon their leader, Francis Libermann.

Although delighted that the group had at last received official recognition and encouragement, in Paris as well as in Rome, Francis hesitated. The way still seemed far from clear. He was not sure about Mauritius; their first objective had been Bourbon and Haiti, well known to his two lieutenants. And for himself, he was anything but sure of his fitness for the priesthood. It would require more waiting, and much prayer, to learn the will of God, as he wrote to Le Vavasseur. There were days when he thought his role must remain only that of organizer; and that thereafter he must seek a life of solitude and prayer. . . .

Perhaps if he made that certain pilgrimage which had long been tempting him—the pilgrimage to the holy House of Loreto—and prayed there, where it was said the Angel had come to Mary, and where his Lord had prayed as a little Child; where His Mother had cared for the household, and

Joseph had worked to provide for it. Perhaps there, in the house where had dwelt the Holy Family, he might receive the guidance for which he yearned.

He knew that great saints had visited it, and had found there the answers to their problems. He would follow the path which led across the high hills to Loreto, which had been trodden by St. Francis of Assisi, by St. Ignatius, St. Francis Xavier, St. Francis Borgia, St. Charles Borromeo, St. Aloysius Gonzaga, St. Francis de Sales, St. Alphonsus Liguori, and many others, to place their petitions at the feet of the Virgin who there had conceived the Divine Word.

He knew there were skeptics, even within the Church, who did not believe the tradition of Loreto. But great popes had sanctioned it; great saints had borne witness to its truth; and great cures of human ills had been effected there. He would not go to seek a cure of his "dear malady"; rather he would gladly suffer it, should that be the Will of God. He would seek only to know that will in regard to his part in the missionary project. . . .

It was a very humble and very poor pilgrim who set out from Rome on foot, one day in the autumn of 1840. Loreto lay on the other side of Italy. As he walked along in his shabby attire—the cloak De la Brunière had given him had now served so many purposes that it was almost as worn out as his soutane—his body thin and emaciated from illness and hunger, he became a figure of derision to more than one child along the way. But when he smiled at them, as he always did, they felt ashamed; and they drew nearer, attracted by the gentleness of the stranger's voice.

He slept in the poorest inns, or with some peasant family

in their humble cottage. And he thought much upon the legend of Loreto—how the name was drawn from that of a great lady, Laureta, who had owned the sylvan wood in Tersatto which lay near the Adriatic, and within whose groves the holy House had first been set down. It was said that angels had borne it across the seas from Nazareth when it had been threatened by the Saracen invasion of Palestine in the year 1291. One night, just before dawn, Italian shepherds had seen a great light in the wood and had found the simple, ancient dwelling where a few hours earlier there had been nothing but an open glade. Holy people had had visions, and messages from Our Lady, that this was indeed the house she had occupied as maiden and as Mother. In the ensuing years devout hands had protected and enclosed the exterior in rich marble, but inside, the humble little stone house with its ancient walls remained as it had been when the Holy Family dwelt there. Now it was sheltered beneath the high dome of a great church, enriched by the priceless gifts of the multitudes of pilgrims who had found their way there.

Perhaps the poorest pilgrim, the son of the Rabbi of Saverne, had now arrived to kneel for hours within those time-darkened walls. Every day for seven days he came back to them. On the seventh day, having lost all sense of time, he left the little house quite late and, moving through the great, dim church, came out under the night sky. The crisp fall air fell upon his face, and he looked upward through the clear atmosphere to a deep sky, bright with myriads of stars. One, just above his head, burned with particular brilliance. "It might be my star," he thought, his heart lifting.

Suddenly a verse from Numbers shot across his mind. "I

shall see him, but not now: I shall behold him, but not nigh: there shall come a star out of Jacob, and a sceptre shall rise out of Israel."

Now the star seemed to glow with an enhanced brightness. And all at once the answer he had sought was vouchsafed. In a flash he knew with certainty that the Lord desired him for His priesthood—that the way would be cleared—and that he must become the veritable leader of *"L'Oeuvre des Noirs."*

Early in January of 1841, just one year after he had arrived in Rome, he set out for Paris, and thence for Strasbourg. The good brother Samson would arrange for his ordination there. Francis was happy in the thought that he would have to spend a few months in the seminary which lay close to the great Cathedral. Once more he would be just an ordinary student of theology, but this time certain of achieving the great objective. And he would be near Samson and Babette.

The six months in the seminary were full of a quiet peace. The cowed enemy never struck. In his heart he came to associate his cure with the finding of that other father in Rome a year ago, who had rested his hand upon his head—and had told him to persevere. And now, like the turning back to an early page, he found himself once more in a seminary—and again giving spiritual counsel to the many, helping the younger souls to find their wings.

It fell out, after all, that Amiens in France, rather than his native Alsace, was to be the scene of his ordination. There, in the private chapel of the episcopal palace, he was ordained to the priesthood on September 18, 1841, at the hands of Bishop Mioland who had offered the young missionary group a house for their novitiate within his diocese. On that day, he signed his joyful letter to Samson and Babette, "F. Libermann, *priest*." For ten long years the letters had borne the humble signature, "*acolyte*." And it had been almost fifteen years since he had first heard the call to his Master's service. After a long and stormy voyage, the port had been reached. He was thirty-nine years old. He had "persevered."

And now at last, free and unfettered, the liberated spirit mounted on ecstatic wings.

About that time, a strange scene was being enacted in far-away Manchuria. The worn missionary who had ventured alone into the distant wild territory of the ferocious "long-haired Tartars" to bring them the knowledge of God sat alone, close to the shore, in the little boat which had propelled him along the Oussouri River. He sat calmly, as he watched them coming for him—yellow faces, slanted eyes, long matted hair. He was ready. But as they waded toward him with their up-held spears, he remembered something.

"Dear God," he prayed, "I did not like his threadbare soutane. (Your garments, too, were threadbare.) I was ashamed, because he was a Jew. (You, too, were a Jew.) In my fastidiousness, I shrank from witnessing his epilepsy—the bloody foam. (Could I have stood at the foot of the Cross, and have watched the blood and water flow from Your side?) . . . That the nephew of the Bishop of Mende—of the ancient line of De la Brunière, no less—should stand before all Rome, as his companion. . . . (Would I have stayed, as companion to the Carpenter of Nazareth?) . . . My piety was offended when, once only, I heard him complain when he felt that You had deserted him. (Master, did You not, there on the Cross, cry out: 'My God, why hast Thou forsaken me?') . . . Take me now, in my repentance, beloved Master. And bless his holy efforts, wherever he may be!"

And then, as the first long lance pierced his breast, he slumped over the side of the little boat. As they swarmed upon him with their knives, he could feel their long, coarse hair falling across his face—the long-haired Tartars whom he had failed to win for Christ. . . .

"My Jesus," he cried, "forgive these children! Forgive me!"

And so died De la Brunière. . . .

Within eight days, Father Libermann, assisted by the saintly Father Desgenettes, and in the presence of Le Vavasseur, Tisserant, and others of the society of the Most Holy Heart of Mary, was offering Mass in Paris at the altar of their beloved shrine, Notre-Dame-des-Victoires. The intention was for the abandoned Negroes, but Francis did not fail to offer a loving memento for their companion, Paul de la Brunière, who with burning zeal had outdistanced them all into the remote pagan lands.

It would be many months more, before they would learn that he was dead.

CHAPTER THIRTEEN

The Mission

THE NUNS OF LOUVENCOURT, of the Holy Hearts of Jesus and Mary, who had befriended Father Libermann, had been happy to prepare the country house at Neuville-les-Amiens for the new missionary society. It lay close to the city near a tributary of the Somme, in a rather poor neighborhood but one strong in the Faith and dotted with other religious houses. The good nuns on very small means, partially supplied by themselves and partially by Father Libermann, had spared no effort to make the abode comfortable and even attractive for the missioners.

Nine days after his ordination, on an afternoon in late September, Francis with his two companions took possession. Le Vavasseur of Bourbon, now a priest, and ever an ascetic, desiring only a life of utmost austerity; and young Marcellin Collin, a jovial Breton who had recently received the subdeaconship, accompanied the founder on a tour of their new domain.

They discovered a small but completely equipped chapel,

a large and lovely garden, and a house of sufficient size to accommodate twelve. But when Le Vavasseur glimpsed the freshly painted furniture in the upstairs bedrooms, he frowned.

"This will never do, Father," he expostulated to Francis. "Missioners should never sleep on anything so grand as these beds. It seems very bad taste on the part of the Sisters who bought them."

"Why, I think the Sisters have been wonderfully kind and charitable," replied Father Libermann mildly.

Le Vavasseur gazed about him in distaste.

"For a young girl's dowry, it might be all right," he protested indignantly, "but for the servants of the poor and the abandoned? It would never do. We should be a scandal to the neighborhood."

And with his large dark eyes flashing, he seized a very pretty and inoffensive little table, and started to throw it out of the window. With difficulty his two companions restrained him.

"My dear Frederic," said Libermann gently, "do you not think it's a good plan to keep the furniture until we have something with which to replace it?"

Collin, in the corner, was doubled up with mirth. But Le Vavasseur's brow did not unfurl, and when the retiring hour came, as Francis and Collin started upstairs to take their repose, each in a comfortable room, he pointedly stretched his slender length out on the hard surface of a long table. There he spent the night.

"That dear boy," confided Francis to Collin, "is so eager to serve the poorest that he imagines he is already with the Negroes of Bourbon. Please help me to get him there soon.

Otherwise, I fear he may have us living without furniture or food."

Tisserant, off in Paris, was chafing that he had to be left behind. Before his ordination the preceding December, the Bishop had promised that as soon as he was ordained, he could fly to his dear Father Libermann and the novitiate at Neuville. But finding that he needed a priest for a certain parish in the city, he had detained him there temporarily. Eugene wrote almost daily to Francis, imploring his prayers that he might soon join them, the quicker to be off for Haiti.

The three who slept in the house that first night were only the advance guard. Gradually, as the weeks passed, others would arrive, and soon the house would be full to brimming over. As for money, it might be said that Our Lady and Francis formed the finance committee. He placed the needs of the small community in her hands; and himself worked indefatigably to stretch over a multitude of necessities the slender sums which fell to him—teaching the others how to market economically, and planning the large vegetable garden he would plant in the spring.

Besides teaching them to market, he must also teach them to cook. They marveled at Father Libermann's skill, while he smiled at the recollection of the hours he had spent as a child with his mother in the kitchen of the old house in Saverne. Often she had permitted him to help; he was surprised himself that he had remembered so much. Soon he had them each taking his turn as chef for the day.

Barring the episode of the young novice who had mistaken the lamp oil for the olive oil, and had served up an odd-tasting salad which they all ate politely without protest; the efficient youth who decided it was a waste of time to cook every day and so had boiled enough vegetables to last for a week, only to discover that they had to be thrown out after the second day; and the young zealot who had been taking lessons from Father Libermann in the art of prayer and one morning got so lost in contemplation in the kitchen that he forgot to light the wood fire until after twelve o'clock, with dinner scheduled for twelve—the meals went well enough.

Adorning the chapel was a beautiful little statue of Our Lady of the Miraculous Medal. It was the gift of Father Desgenettes, of their cherished Notre-Dame-des-Victoires. Mass and an exact schedule of prayer and devotions filled many hours of the day. In the evening Father Libermann read aloud from the Rule he had so carefully composed in Rome. Then did the compelling power of his spirituality touch them most. They thought they had never been happier than at Neuville, dreaming of the love and salvation they would soon be carrying to the poor Negroes.

Only Le Vavasseur seemed troubled. The Rule was not strict enough. The task upon which they were embarking would require men of iron; the novitiate should put that iron into their souls. The more practical founder knew there must be nourishment and strength in the bodies of the men he would send to far places. And he insisted on long periods of walking in the open air, no matter what the weather.

Actually the first missioner to leave France was a member of the community only in spirit. He had known Francis in Issy, and once having talked with him, had determined in his heart to join the work for the Negroes as soon as the society should be launched. But as he waited as a priest in his small native diocese of Evreux, Bishop Collier of the island of Mauritius again sent out an appeal from Paris for missionaries.

Three months before the novitiate at Neuville had opened, Jacques Désiré Laval had joined him. But not before turning over a portion of his fortune to Father Libermann for *L'Oeuvre des Noirs.*

The noble pattern which Laval came to set in Mauritius, his holy life and the amazing results he accomplished, proved to be the model which Francis, as the story unfolded, exhorted his sons to follow. Often he told them that this was the man who, in the world, had been a successful doctor, a lover of society—and of horses. One day, while riding a fiery thoroughbred, he had been thrown and had lain for weeks, suffering from serious injuries. As with Ignatius centuries earlier, the long confinement had turned his thoughts toward God. As soon as he was able to walk again, he renounced that world in which he had cut such a splendid figure, and entered the seminary. . . .

By early spring the house at Neuville was full. Bouchet and Roussel had come; Audebert and Bureau; Saint-Abin and Boisdron; de Régnier and Blampin; and the more mature Abbé Bessieux. Almost every post brought Francis new appeals for admission. He told Our Lady that she would have to build them an additional wing or two and enlarge the chapel. By March the work was under way.

That restless spirit, Le Vavasseur, was actually one of the first two to leave the novitiate for the mission field. With a companion, his urgent steps were bent toward Bourbon where he arrived with Boisdron in June of 1842. Almost the first person they encountered was an elderly, experienced missioner of the ancient Congregation of the Holy Ghost, which had been established in Paris in 1703—especially to carry salvation to the Negroes. The French Revolution had so thoroughly dispersed it that the young missioners from Neuville were amazed to find any of its men still laboring in the mission field.

Meanwhile Francis was pulling every string to secure assignments in the colonies for his ardent missioners. He journeyed to Paris constantly for long interviews with the Ministry of Colonies which kept its supervisory hand upon the missions—a matter which involved diplomacy with native governments. His correspondence, conducted mainly in his room, was necessarily prolific. From the start, he had insisted upon taking the least desirable room in the house for himself—one that was frigid in winter and torrid in summer.

The fall of 1842 was unusually cold, and the house had no heat except that which emanated from the kitchen stove. One night in October, Francis, who had retired to write some letters, found that after an hour or so his fingers had become so numbed that he could scarcely hold the pen. He picked up his writing materials and stole softly down the stairs, spreading his work out on the kitchen table. He was busily engaged in a letter to Le Vavasseur, who had written in some discouragement about the confused political situation in Bourbon, when he heard the front door—never locked—fling open. He raised his head, knowing that the only light in the house was in the kitchen, and that the visitor would be drawn toward it. In another instant, Tisserant stood upon the threshold. They embraced with joy, each talking at once.

"Eugene! I did not know—"

"I wanted to surprise you, Father. The Bishop has finally released me. I can now make my novitiate in Neuville!"

Francis held him off at arm's length, and looked at him smilingly.

"Not for long, *mon ami*, as much as I should desire it! Look—"

He turned to the table and picked up an official document.

"Months ago, knowing your ardor, and wishing to find an early post for one of the founders of *L'Oeuvre des Noirs*, I began negotiations about sending you to Haiti. Look! The permission came this morning—sooner than I had anticipated. They have stated that it is desirable that you should leave for Haiti next month."

Tisserant sat down with a happy sigh.

"I can thank *Notre Dame des Victoires*," he said simply. "I have not left her a moment's peace." . . .

There were a few happy weeks with his leader, but by mid-November Eugene was off to his long-cherished goal, to redeem the Negroes of his native land whose sufferings and misery had touched him from childhood.

Thus had the two Creoles who had importuned Francis on that long-ago day in the arbor at Issy—and but for whom he would perhaps not now be engaged in this work—realized their dream, Frederic, in Bourbon; Eugene, in Haiti. The first missioners of the Society of the Holy Heart of Mary were launched. Francis breathed easier.

While at the seminary in Strasbourg, he had made a new friend—a young Alsatian seminarian, Ignatius Schwindenhammer, who, like a veritable member of the Issy bands of piety, had been drawn to seek his spiritual counsel. On parting, the youth had promised to enter Neuville as soon as ordained. Now he too had arrived to swell the young community. Francis rejoiced greatly, finding in him not only a deeply spiritual nature and a fine intellect, but a practical turn of mind as well which helped to balance a house almost entirely dominated by the lively Gallic temperament, full of genius and ardor but at times strongly individualistic. There was something in his very name—Schwindenhammer—which suggested method and calm.

Father Libermann had sent others out to assist Tisserant in Haiti; but the news from there and from Bourbon was far from satisfactory. Local political disturbances made it difficult for the missioners to function, and it seemed a question whether or not it was wise to permit his men to remain. Meanwhile the novitiate had become literally thronged with eager aspirants to the mission field. Where to send them?

In his perplexity, Francis journeyed to Paris in December of 1842, on a pilgrimage to Notre-Dame-des-Victoires who had never failed them—and to consult his friend there, the Abbé Desgenettes. After making his prayer before the altar, he was descending the steps of the church when he encountered the Abbé, who immediately asked for news of Neuville.

"*Mon père*," said Francis, "we are greatly embarrassed."

"But, how is that?"

"We have no territory."

"You mean, you have no money?"

"Oh, no! Our Lady never permits us to be in want of that. But we do not know where to go. On every side, mission doors seem closed to us."

The kindly Abbé tried to console him, and led him in to his warm hearthside. When they were seated, Francis said:

"I'm most grateful for your sympathy—but do you know, it's a strange thing—"

He broke off to gaze reflectively into the fire. The Abbé waited.

"Even though I now find myself with five who have completed their novitiate," Francis continued, "five impatient young missioners, restless over the long delays and indefinite postponements, all as eager as young tigers to be off—somehow just now I do not feel the slightest anxiety."

"And how do you account for that?"

"It has just come to me—a feeling that at this very moment Our Lady is preparing a mission for us."

That afternoon, having taken leave of his old friend and paid a hurried visit to Felkel, Francis left Paris for Amiens and the novitiate.

Father Desgenettes was very busy in the evening with numerous callers; and when early the next morning before he had said Mass a visitor from America was announced, the matter of the missioners at Neuville was far from his thoughts. His visitor proved to be Bishop Barron who had just been consecrated in Rome and appointed vicar apostolic of the two Guineas in Africa, where he had already spent some time at the behest of the American Church. He was stopping in Paris on his way back, to recruit missionaries for his vast diocese.

Desgenettes listened sympathetically to his plea, but it was not until the elderly Abbé stood before the altar of Notre-Dame-des-Victoires—the same altar where he had once, at the nadir of discouragement, received that whispered word to dedicate his church to Mary's Immaculate Heart—that he thought of Father Libermann's need. Here was a man looking for missionaries, and at Amiens there were men looking for missions. Immediately after Mass he apprised the delighted Bishop Barron, and sent word to Francis to return at once to Paris.

From the start, the two were much drawn to each other—

the slender Abbé who seemed to wear the peace of angels, and the tall Edward Barron of Ballyneal, who had gone out from Ireland to America. Having left an older brother who was a baronet and a member of Parliament, he had joined the American secular clergy. Just then the American Church was greatly concerned about the slaves who, having been liberated by certain humane masters in the States, had returned to their ancestral land and were struggling along in Liberia. Appeals had been made to some of the religious congregations to send men, but they had fallen upon deaf ears. Only two priests had volunteered, both from the secular clergy. One of them was Edward Barron.

"I knew," Francis said happily to him, "before I left Paris the other day, that Our Lady was in process of providing us with a mission where we could serve our dear Negroes."

Not long after Francis had gone back to Amiens, the Bishop returned his visit, arriving at Neuville for further discussions. He was very happy about the splendid material he found there, and felt he could not have asked for finer young men. On their part, they could scarcely believe their good fortune. Their companions had gone to Bourbon and Haiti—but what were those "civilized" spots, compared to the field they would find on the great Dark Continent itself?

Early in the days of the novitiate, Francis had welcomed selfless young men who wished to serve the missions but yet did not feel themselves called to the priesthood. These had been organized into a group of coadjutor Brothers. He resolved now to send three of them with the mission to Africa. Before it got under way there were seven priests ready to go —Bessieux, De Régnier, Audebert, Roussel, Bouchet, Maurice and Paul Laval, who by chance bore the same name as the brilliant pioneer of Mauritius. Their good father equipped them well.

It was September of 1843 when they embarked for Africa.

Francis, laboring on at his novitiate, training and despatching others to far lands, was heavy with the presentiment of tragedy. Months had elapsed since he had heard from his African group. Had they written and the letters not reached him? He could only pray—and try to throw off the unaccountable shadow which had fallen athwart his heart.

At length in October of 1844, more than a year after they had departed aglow with the hope of the high deeds they would accomplish, a letter came from Bishop Barron. Francis' hands trembled so that he could hardly open it. Yes, there it was—the calamitous news. The letter had been written two months previously. Of that brave young company, five were dead, having perished one after the other from the strange, terrible fevers of the Dark Continent. Barron himself was abandoning the field. The brave Bessieux and another were remaining to hold the mission for the Society of the Holy Heart of Mary. The others were returning to France. . . .

The founder buried his head in his hands and wept. He had sent them forth to their deaths. And the letter stated that De Régnier, one of his first sons, had died whispering a message to their father in France: "Tell him—that I am happy to have left everything for our Divine Master—and that if I had it to do over again, I would do it a thousand times! . . . Courage, very dear father; when everything seems lost, it is then that Our Lady shows herself. Whether we live, or whether we die, we belong to God—to God and to Mary." . . .

Grief hung heavy upon the novitiate at Neuville, and as the

somber days passed, Francis, brooding upon the tragedy, became certain that a demon lurked in the mission field of
Guinea—a demon who had taken five of his bravest. But he
would yet conquer that demon! . . .

He had sent men to Mauritius; and now was looking toward
Madagascar. Still the aspirants were pouring in; he did not
have enough missions for them all.

Every now and again his men would write that they had
encountered a missionary of the Congregation of the Holy
Ghost—and he marveled at the virility of that ancient society
which, with scarcely a shell of organization left, still had a
few experienced missioners laboring among the Negroes.
When they died, what would happen? Would not that old
and honorable name become merely a memory?

As he studied the reports from his sons, he became convinced that the Church must eventually establish a native
clergy and hierarchy to serve their own people. His missioners should plant the acorn which would take root and at length
stretch heavenward in just such a lasting and mighty oak. His
men must not only spread the Faith, but must establish
schools and encourage agriculture, the trades, and the arts.
From such soil would a native clergy grow. It was a far-
reaching dream—but he was pledged to it.

So many new applicants were knocking at the doors of
Neuville that in 1844 Francis was obliged to establish a new
house at near-by Noyon. It was soon to be followed by another in Bordeaux. Religious souls who for one reason or another could not apply for admission to his group, and men
and women of the world continued to write to him for guidance. Always his basic theme was peace. To one troubled by
a withdrawal of grace, he wrote:

"Be not discouraged, but leave all in the hands of God, and of Mary—and keep yourself in peace. God is with you, I am certain; and you are with God. Let that be sufficient."

And to another:

"The infallible means of being in continual mental prayer is to possess one's soul in peace before our Lord. Be attentive to this saying: 'to possess one's soul in peace.' It was employed by our Divine Master Himself."

Now students with vocations to the priesthood, but who were not yet ordained, were applying. Father Libermann established new courses for these; and with his conviction that the strength of the Church stemmed eternally from Rome, accented the study of canon law and of the liturgy—both of which had been somewhat neglected in France.

Eugene Tisserant, that first eager disciple, had been writing increasingly discouraged letters from Haiti where present conditions made it almost impossible to carry on his work. Of late, his health had begun to fail, so his ever-solicitous leader wrote him and his companions to return to France. Haiti would never be abandoned, but it was plain that their Master had His own plans in regard to that mission, and wished them to wait a little.

The group arrived at the mother house in May of 1845, just when the fruit trees which Francis had planted in the garden were white with blossoms. The garden had actually become a veritable farm, which supplied them not only with vegetables, but with milk from their own cow, and eggs from their brood of chickens. There were also pigs, pigeons, and a sturdy old horse. Under Father Libermann's wise economy, the men baked their own bread and made their own wine.

When Francis joyfully welcomed Tisserant, inwardly his

heart ached at the sight of the lively Creole, worn thin and ill from his discouraging labors. And he enjoined a long rest in Provence. . . .

Father Libermann had sent Ignatius Schwindenhammer to Rome to propose the establishment of a house in Europe for the training of promising young Negroes who could return as priests to their native soil—the forerunners of that indigenous clergy of which he dreamed. The Propaganda acknowledged the project as excellent, but it was not as easy to launch as it might seem.

During all this time, with a spirit that raced ahead of his limited strength, Francis found that the old headaches, encouraged by the fatigues of his journeys to Paris and to Rome; to his other houses; his endless negotiations and correspondence, his problems of administration, were again attacking relentlessly. Frequently they affected his vision. There were times when he felt so ill that he could not sleep. Then he would lie awake, finding solace and mystery in the wind which would arise in the stillness from nowhere, to sing its rhapsody through the trees and against his casement window.

"The signal of the Holy Spirit," he would murmur.

Had not the wind, which puts animation into all nature, preceded the tongues of flame on that first Pentecost? And He who held the wind in His hands was guarding the holy young souls within the house whose direction was his privilege.

These however began to worry about the increasing ill health of their beloved father. They even made him sign a solemn pledge that he would guard himself more carefully.

Into that unprotesting signature were spun his basic humility and obedience. . . .

Through the courage of Bessieux, and the careful planning of the founder who had sent reinforcements, the decimated mission in Guinea had survived. And now Francis won the consent of Rome to name one of his men for appointment as vicar apostolic. Bessieux, having declined the post in all humility, Francis turned to Tisserant, whose early call to the missions, and labors and hard experience in Haiti, had well qualified him. Letters from Provence having assured Father Libermann that the missioner's health was well restored, he sent him the good tiding. On its receipt Eugene's spirit soared upward on wings of joy. So eager was he to reach his new apostolate that he sacrificed a visit to his beloved leader and to his friends in Paris, and made straight for the nearest port and the first ship sailing for Africa.

"The others whom you have appointed to accompany me can follow as quickly as they are able," he wrote to Father Libermann.

Francis, who was alone in his room on that gray November morning of the year 1845 when the letter arrived, laid it down with a smile in which there was affection and amusement. There was no occasion to doubt the zeal of this son! It would have lifted his heart to see him again—but the haste and the ardor were even greater cause for rejoicing. On the Dark Continent which had brought them so much tragedy, Tisserant would banish that haunting demon and solidify the great work begun by Bessieux.

But sitting there at his simple table, reflecting on the foothold they would gain in Africa, all at once it seemed to Francis as though the room were suddenly engulfed in a great darkness. He clutched the edge of the table to still the trembling of his hands, wondering in terror if. . . . Immediately it seemed that his ears were full of a great roaring. It was like —yes, it was like the roaring of the sea. In a moment it had passed, and the room had lightened again. Obviously, this had not been the ancient enemy. But it had been something —something that Francis resolutely shoved to the back of his mind and resolved not to mention.

The good ship *Papin* left port toward the end of November. As it rode the wintry seas, Father Tisserant made friends with passengers and crew, and talked to them of God. Thoughtful of others, every day he busied himself with a thousand kindnesses. There was a very likable Jewish merchant aboard, one Samuel Marx, who was attracted by the tall young missioner, and frequently sought him out. The two had many a religious discussion as they watched the black seas rolling by. But Eugene thought that he had never encountered a mind so solidly sealed against the Christian idea. . . .

Toward midnight on the sixth of December, the *Papin* began to pitch and toss, and suddenly rode right into the heart of a hurricane. People were thrown violently from their bunks, the deck was awash, and the ship seemed to be flung along upon her side. Just off the coast of Mogador, and amidst the shouts and gigantic efforts of an harassed captain and crew, the *Papin*, out of all control, thudded against a sand bar. As the high seas beat upon her mercilessly, she began to fall apart.

It was with one accord that the terrified passengers gathered in the cabin about the missioner of the Congregation of the Holy Heart of Mary. That inner peace on the dark young face to which they had been drawn was even more evident now. With the ship trembling violently, and with the roar of the surging waters all about them, he knelt for a brief silent prayer. Then rising, he began to speak calmly, consolingly, to one hundred and fifty panic-stricken human beings. Invoking the aid of Mary, he prayed in the name of all for the grace to die as good Christians. His voice, his manner, quieted them. Then he blessed them all, and gave them general absolution. One by one, they had dropped to their knees. And now the ocean was seeping into the cabin.

All at once Eugene saw his friend Marx making his way to him through the kneeling throng.

"If I were to receive baptism, is it really true that God would pardon my sins, and accept me?"

"But surely, my friend."

"Then I implore you, baptize me," cried the other, "for I believe!"

One there was in that throng, making his last peace with God, who was able to stagger to his feet and find his way to a carafe of drinking water which, held fast in a wall bracket, had miraculously preserved some of its contents. He brought the water to Father Tisserant—and there, before the now silent and prayerful group, baptism was bestowed upon the merchant. And just then, as though to mark dramatically the completion of the ceremony, the sea rushed in. . . .

The Creole and the Jew, with the name of Jesus upon their lips, perished together. Seventy-five others were also cast to their deaths. The remainder somehow struggled to shore.

It was from several of these, writing in gratitude for the heroism of the missionary, that Francis eventually heard the whole tragic but magnificent story. He wept both from sor-

row and from joy. Truly had one of the two first disciples
given his life for *L'Oeuvre des Noirs*—had died as a true son
of the company of the Holy Heart of Mary. And as Francis
took his grief to the foot of the Cross, he did not forget that
Tisserant, before dying, had brought salvation to one of his
own people. He would miss that impetuous disciple, with his
burning zeal, more than his other children would ever guess.

In the heavy days that ensued, Francis reflected sadly that
the demon bent upon destroying his mission in Guinea remained still unconquered. Six lives—it was six too many. But
he would end by slaying that demon, no matter what the cost.

Accordingly, he traveled down to Rome to plead before
the Propaganda for his cherished but seemingly ill-fated mission. He did it so successfully that the result was the creation
of a new vicariate apostolic, comprising the two Guineas and
Senegambia, and extending along the coast of Africa for
1,200 leagues—and into the interior without limit. In 1847,
the Abbé Truffet, whose call to the Society of the Holy Heart
of Mary had come to him while kneeling in Notre-Dame-des-
Victoires, was appointed vicar apostolic of the wide territory.

But alas, the demon was still unconquered. Truffet had not
been at his post for more than six months when he was attacked by the fatal fever, and died within a few days. But
during his short stay among the natives he had won their love
to such an extent that Francis, upon hearing of their inconsolable grief, felt constrained to write to their ruler, Eliman,
the King of Dakar:

"The blessing and benediction of God, the Father and
Giver of all Creatures! . . . My heart has been broken with
sorrow, not alone because I have lost in the good bishop a
very dear friend, but especially because you no longer possess

him who loved you all so tenderly—who loved all the Negroes. I wish you could see the afflictions of my heart; for my
heart is yours—my heart belongs to the Africans. . . ."

So it fell out that in the end it was Bessieux, of the remarkable tenacity, and now rich in years of experience, who perforce took over the administration of the mission in Guinea.
There with his assistant, Kobés, he made certain for all time
the congregation's achievement on the Dark Continent. After
five terrible years, the "demon of Guinea" had been slain. . . .

In all the dark shadows which had oppressed Francis' soul
during the anxious years of 1846 and 1847, he had met also
his share of sunshine. Late in 1846 he had been able to acquire, through selling the beloved but outgrown cradle of
Neuville, the ancient Cistercian abbey of Notre-Dame-du-
Gard, hallowed by St. Bernard himself, and whose first stones
had been laid in the year 1139. Abandoned during the French
Revolution, it had been restored in 1818—only again to be
deserted in 1832 when a new railway threatened to cut across
its still peace. It lay, with all its spirit of sanctity and picturesque beauty, but fourteen miles from Neuville. There Father
Libermann moved his family; and there also, established the
senior scholasticate of the Congregation of the Holy Heart of
Mary.

Rome was beginning to look upon the converted Alsatian
Jew laboring in France, the erstwhile epileptic, as something
of a wonder. Little more than seven years had elapsed since
his ordination—since the opening of his novitiate—and already he had established three other houses, and his society
was playing a leading role in the work of the missions. The
Council of the Propaganda deliberated; and one day for-

warded to the founder a somewhat startling suggestion.
Would Father Libermann not consider uniting his congregation with that of the ancient Congregation of the Holy Ghost?

Both societies had been founded to carry salvation to the
Negroes—one in 1703, the other in 1841. The older had long
ago established its work in the colonies where Father Libermann's sons were now laboring with such distinction and elbow to elbow with some of the Holy Ghost missioners—to be
sure, few in number. The administration of the older congregation, fallen to pieces under the blows of the Revolution, had
never sufficiently recovered. It needed an administrator like
Father Libermann.

In Paris lay its old mother house, hallowed and historic. It
was headed by Father Monnet who only longed to return
to his beloved mission field of Madagascar to die there among
the natives he loved. The rule and constitutions of Father
Libermann's congregation would admirably serve to cover an
amalgamation of the two societies. The ancient would benefit
by an able administration and the influx of the eager young
souls of the Congregation of the Holy Heart of Mary. The
newer would benefit by the approbation, favor, and privileges
long enjoyed by the ancient society at the hands of the French
government.

Francis sat down and took a long breath. In truth, for some
six years he had been trying to evolve a plan of closer coop-
eration between his men and those of the old congregation.

Pope Pius IX's nuncio in Paris was commissioned to urge
Father Libermann to adopt the suggestion. Within his soul,
Francis wondered what his special Holy Father, Gregory
XVI—he who had placed his gentle hand upon his head on
that day eight years before and had told him to "persevere"—

would have thought of the suggestion. He had mourned the death of this father in 1846. Now he would ask for his prayers in heaven—and would lay his problem at the feet of *Notre Dame des Victoires.*

After long vigils and prayer, he received his answer. He felt convinced that the proposed fusion would be pleasing to his beloved Master. There remained but one stumbling block. It had been urged that the amalgamation should preserve the name of the older society. The founder of the Congregation of the Holy Heart of Mary saw nothing objectionable in this. But how could he in combining the two societies omit the name of Our Lady to whose intercession he and his sons owed everything? They had dedicated themselves to her. Would not his sons grieve if her name were omitted? He had a very deep devotion to the Holy Spirit—to Him who breathed upon the souls of men in the song of the wind.

Hence he made a counterproposition that the fusion be formally named "The Congregation of the Holy Ghost and of the Holy Heart of Mary." So it was determined. After many conferences in Paris between Father Libermann and his assistants with representatives of the older society and the nuncio—conferences at which Francis' tact and diplomatic genius unobtrusively smoothed away the thorns of sacrifice with which the change was naturally bestrewn—the union was formally sanctioned by Rome on September 26, 1848.

Father Monnet, Superior of the Congregation of the Holy Ghost, resigned quite happily to resume his role of simple missionary to Madagascar—and Father Libermann was unanimously elected first Superior-General of the new congregation. With his grace and gentleness, with that smile which had ever been irresistible, he had succeeded in uniting all hearts under the time-honored motto of the old society: *"Cor Unum et Anima Una*—One Heart and One Spirit."

He arrived in Paris to take over his new mother house, accompanied by the methodical Ignatius Schwindenhammer, on a clear, crisp October evening. After a visit to Notre-Dame-des-Victoires, they found their way to the ancient Seminary of the Holy Ghost. Night had fallen, and as Francis paused before the worn stone steps, he gazed upward at the old walls which had witnessed almost a century and a half of the turbulent history of Paris. They had survived the days of the Terror, the revolution of 1830—and still stood firm. The breath of the Holy Spirit had preserved them.

His gaze followed upward to the high turreted roof, and beyond into the deep velvety heavens. There! He might have known it. For in that far depth, and directly above the topmost turret, hung one brilliant star. "It is the same which shone above Loreto," he murmured to himself. The star of Jacob continued to guide him. He mounted the steps with a high heart.

During the next days, as he walked through the halls of the famous old building, it seemed to him that often there was an unseen companion at his side. For the thought of Claude Poullart des Places, the founder of the Holy Ghost Congregation, was vividly with him—that handsome young Frenchman who, gifted and wealthy, had once startled the gay city by renouncing a promising career in law to study for the priesthood. Widely differing had been their birth and worldly associations, but they were united as brothers by something stronger than these—their devotion to the cause of the Negroes. That, and another curious affinity—the fact that each in his zeal had labored to found a missionary congregation long before either had achieved ordination to the priesthood. Des Places, at the head of his already successful society, had lived scarcely three years after his ordination.

How many years were yet to be allotted to the son of the Rabbi of Saverne? Within his heart, he did not think many. He had a feeling that it would be little more than three. . . . He must hasten to cement the foundations, to perfect the work his good Master had set him—while there was yet time.

There were journeys to his several houses to be regularly undertaken, to say nothing of those to Rome where a vast amount of labor waited to secure the establishment of the bishoprics he wanted for Martinique, Guadaloupe, and Bourbon—such as he had already won for Guinea. There were negotiations to be conducted with foreign governments, with visiting dignitaries, and with the ministries of the various departments of the French government which, under the presidency of Louis Napoleon, was just then emerging from another period of chaos. He knew that in administering his congregation, politically he would have to walk a wary way.

Nor was the ecclesiastical way any path of roses. Archbishop Sibour of Paris, found himself at variance with Rome over the departure from the ancient constitutions which had placed the Congregation of the Holy Ghost under the immediate jurisdiction of the Archbishop. Rome desired that the fusion should be primarily subject to the Holy See, with the Archbishop retaining only normal jurisdiction. Francis was caught between the two, desiring above all to be subject to Rome, but inconsolable over the necessity of opposing his archbishop. Nevertheless the skill with which he navigated the dangerous shoals was winning him the respect of the highest officials of Church and State. He had won a legion of powerful friends who had come to regard him not only as a man of great sanctity, but also as a consummate administrator.

From the start of his residence within the walls of the great seminary, he had been sought out for counsel and charity by poor and rich, peasant and aristocrat, followers and leaders, men and women. He had helped in the guidance of more than one religious congregation of women . . . and had given his devoted help to the Little Sisters of the Poor. Soon the old halls had become the rendezvous of learned ecclesiastics of many other congregations and of the secular clergy who had learned to appreciate the scholarship of the Rabbi's son who was the Superior-General of the Holy Ghost Fathers.

About a large table at which he presided, brilliant discussions took place, and great plans were matured. There were many who remembered him in his student days at Saint-Sulpice and Issy—the impoverished young man with the tragic malady to whom ordination seemed forever denied. They remembered him as he had swept the walks of the Solitude, carrying out the most menial chores. Had anyone prophesied then that this one would some day be the Superior-General of a great missionary congregation and himself the head of an ancient seminary in Paris, he would have been taken for a fool.

But vast labors had begun to exact their toll of a slender body, never strong, battered by long illnesses which had only been defeated by that unconquerable burning flame ever animating the spirit. Cholera again struck Paris in the spring of 1849. It was not however this dreaded scourge that attacked Francis, but rather a strange recurrent fever which no treatment seemed able to allay. He thought that by quitting Paris and journeying into the country to the scenes of the congregation's now wide-flung interests, he would throw it off.

He had scarcely been gone a month when he was stricken by a more serious affliction—the news that his beloved Felkel, whose companionship in Paris had meant so much to him, had succumbed to the cholera. The great heart faltered. For days he moved about in silence. . . . None but the brothers Libermann themselves understood the love which had ever united them. None, that is, save that Brother who hung upon His Cross. And it was He who renewed the courage within the feverish, depleted body and stricken soul.

But before this Francis, convinced that his own death was imminent, had dictated a letter recalling to France that one remaining first disciple—Frederic Le Vavasseur. As a missioner in Bourbon, he had covered himself with glory. Now, before it was too late, Frederic must return to learn the progress and the plans of that work for the Negroes which he and Tisserant had actually launched under the trees of Issy and which had grown to such noble proportions.

After the letter had been sent Francis rested easier and, though still a victim of the mysterious fever, was able to reach Strasbourg and the arms of Samson and Babette, and the beloved family. He grew better upon learning that one of the nephews, named for him and for St. Francis Xavier, wished to become a priest and a missioner of the Congregation of the Holy Ghost and the Holy Heart of Mary. Samson's son! To complete his joy there was the revelation that three of his nieces were planning to enter the religious life. There, among his own, he gathered strength. Under his older brother's loving care, the fever left him at the end of the summer, and by mid-September he was able to return to Paris.

Plunging again into his manifold activities, and with Ignatius assisting him, he counted the days until Le Vavasseur would arrive. It was a long wait, and his health again faltered. Due to some unavoidable delays, it was not until February of 1850 that he looked again into the flashing dark eyes of his early disciple. The very sight of him—the long and good story of Bourbon—filled Francis with a new strength and made him almost merry.

On that first day of his son's return, they were seated in his lofty study. A plate of fruit, left that morning at the door by a pious lady, one of his penitents, had been placed upon the desk. The plate was a pretty thing of Dresden—all gay flowers, with a lacey, gilt-edged rim.

"Have some fruit, my dear Frederic," urged Libermann, offering him the plate.

"Thank you, Father," replied the missioner, breaking off a few grapes.

"And," remarked Francis Libermann with a twinkle, "try to forgive the little plate, and don't throw it out of the window. It can't help itself for being gay. It really does not mean any harm."

A sober young seminarian who just then passed the open door was surprised at the laughter which rang out from the Superior's study.

"I see that you have not forgotten Neuville," said Frederic. "What a rigid young ass I was! But Bourbon has taught me to be more tolerant."

"I hope so, my dear friend," said Francis gently. . . .

Actually Le Vavasseur was filled with anxiety as he looked into the good father's face—even thinner than when he had last seen it. It did indeed bear that indefinable sign of the approach of the Dark Angel. He hoped he could remain for a while. It was good to be with his leader, with his brothers, again.

It proved to be a longer stay than he had anticipated. He was kept extremely busy, both in Paris and at the other houses. Abroad, the missions were flourishing, and the work of administration was vast.

Early in December of 1851, Francis journeyed to the ancient spot he loved, Notre-Dame-du-Gard. He had felt weary and ill on the journey, and as soon as the old gray abbey walls came into sight, he knew that he would have to seek his bed. Anxious, devoted hands cared for him throughout the ensuing weeks. And when Christmas came, the normal jubilations were muted. Their founder lay ill in the infirmary. Young voices were lowered, footsteps softened. The doctor looked grave—and pronounced it a serious malady of the liver.

Francis grew restless with the attentions they showered upon him, and firmly sent them back to their religious devotions. Lying there alone in the darkened room, he quietly prayed to be permitted to return to Paris and the seminary which had been placed in his care, that he might discharge some last duties.

To the surprise of all, he gained sufficient strength to undertake the journey shortly after Christmas. But by the time he had reached Paris and the seminary, he was very weak. Anxiously Le Vavasseur supported him to his room.

"My dear son," murmured Francis, "it is you who will take care of me now at the end."

They hoped that under the best physicians Paris could offer, he would rally—but hope soon turned to despair. Many were those who sought an excuse to enter the room where the Superior lay. In the heart of each, no matter how humble his role in the great edifice, rested the memory of the kindnesses he had bestowed at times when most needed. They wished to receive fresh inspiration from the patience with which he silently endured terrible physical suffering.

Either Le Vavasseur or Ignatius, who was now Superior of Notre-Dame-du-Gard and who had hastened to Paris, was constantly at his side. To these, in his less painful hours, Father Libermann confided his plans for the future of the congregation. When they asked him, in all the simple humility he had taught them, which of the two should in the end assume his duties, he had turned first to one, and then to the other with the familiar winning smile. At length it was to Ignatius that he murmured:

"I think it is *you* who must sacrifice yourself."

Then he had reached out and clasped Frederic's hand. He said: "But you are ever my first disciple; and I will be with you always." . . .

They sent for Samson toward the end of January. With heavy heart the oldest of the brothers Libermann hastened from Strasbourg. Jacob was dying. No, not Jacob, but the little "Shaekle" whom he had helped to bring up. When he approached the sickbed, he gathered the frail wasted form in his arms.

Ignatius, heartbroken, was sending daily reports to Notre-Dame-du-Gard and imploring the prayers of the community for a miracle. When told of this, Francis smiled lovingly.

"Tell them," he whispered, "that I do not forget them; that I shall never forget them."

A moment later he sighed, and reached out for Samson's hand.

"It is you who have run the good course," he murmured, "you and Babette. You were the first. Let us pray now for the others, wherever they may be—David and Henoch, Samuel and Esther. Felkel is already in heaven. And let us pray, too, for dear Isaac and Sarah." . . .

The word had passed through Paris that Father Libermann was dying. Those who were left of the old friends hastened to his bedside. The aged Abbé Desgenettes came; and others. And one said to another:

"Come; let us go and see how a saint dies." . . .

One evening when his sons were gathered about him, they begged him to tell them what they should do to be good religious. His voice was very weak now, and he spoke between long pauses.

"Be fervent—above all, practice charity. . . . Sacrifice yourselves for Jesus—for Jesus alone. . . . Sacrifice with Mary. . . . God is all. . . . Man is nothing."

On a morning in late January he received his last earthly Communion, and the last Sacraments were administered. Samson was there, Le Vavasseur and Ignatius.

And now there was silence in the death chamber, except for the beating of the cold winter rain against the windows. Their father lay with his head partially raised, his sensitive Semitic profile etched against the white pillow. His gentle eyes were fixed upon the crucifix they had arranged at the foot of his bed. Soon the lids closed, and his heavy breathing told them that he was far away. . . .

He was a child again, in the old house in Saverne; and he and his mother were playing a game, hiding from the others a red crayon which Samson had brought him. Now he was with his father in the study, bent over the wonderful book with the pictures of the ships and the rescues at sea; and he could feel his father's hand stroking his head. . . . Then Felkel and he were chasing each other through the house. . . . Again he was lying on his back on the grass beside Samson, watching the treetops bend to the wind—the mysteriously beautiful Wind. . . . Of a sudden, he was in the synagogue, reading aloud from the Torah—and his father was smiling. . . .

This was a big city. Yes, it was Metz, for there was the Rabbi Scholom standing at a door and shaking his head. . . . The scene changed to a tavern; he and Lazarus sat there, near the fire, laughing and sipping their wine. But it was getting too warm there near the roaring fire; he must move. . . .

The prayerful watchers in the death chamber saw the wasted form stir slightly. . . .

Now he was in a stagecoach on his way to Paris, and the wheels under him were singing an endless refrain: "Deutz or Drach, Deutz or Drach—" . . . Here now was a lovely, silent little chapel. On his knees before the altar, suddenly he saw his old friend, the Abbé Augé—and felt a great glow of happiness. He had come to baptize him! . . .

Le Vavasseur, close to the bedside, saw the ghost of a smile pass over the emaciated face. . . .

Ah, who was this stout farmer, shouting and gesticulating on a country road? He was pointing to a lot of vegetables strewn about at their feet. If he could only purchase them for the seminary! Father Mollevaut would be pleased. . . . Now he was walking under a green canopy of arching trees, with Le Vavasseur at his right, and Tisserant at his left. But suddenly a great wave of the sea rolled over them from nowhere

—and when it receded only he and Le Vavasseur were left. He wept. . . .

Of a sudden, he was in the novitiate at Rennes, and the Abbé Louis was shaking a long finger at him. Suffering and ill, he lay in the infirmary, a bandage upon his head. Would the novices all desert him? . . .

The watchers noticed that the sleeper sighed ever so slightly. . . .

This would be Notre-Dame-des-Victoires, for he was lying prostrate before the altar. . . . Father Pinault had come in, and was consoling him. . . . Here all at once was a great, magnificent chamber. He was on his knees, and the smiling Drach was at his side. Ah, there came the wondrous figure in white for whom they waited. He glided straight to Francis, and put his hand upon his head. . . .

But what was all this fluttering about his face? Ah, yes; it was nothing but the pigeons in the loft, come for their supper. He crumbled the bread and tossed it to them. . . . Now he was on a highroad, walking, walking—so weary. Ah, there it was! The great cathedral which sheltered the tiny house. If he could but summon strength to pull himself within, he would find peace there. . . .

Le Vavasseur heard his breath come more rapidly. . . .

He had achieved it! Now he knelt within those ancient, sacred walls. . . . Suddenly he heard the sonorous Latin words of the Bishop of Amiens, ordaining him. . . .

Those in the room heard him sigh, as though a great weight had been lifted from him. . . .

Now he was planting fruit trees in the garden of Neuville. How soon would they bear fruit to feed his hungry children?

. . . Then he stood, gazing up at the magnificent old abbey of Notre-Dame-du-Gard. . . . All at once, he seemed to be in some dark, far land, weeping, and passing from sickbed to sickbed. One, two, three, four, five—his children. . . . Presently he was facing the great Seminary of the Holy Ghost.

He stood before the Propaganda in Rome, urging, pleading. They nodded and smiled. It would be all right, they assured him—all right with his congregation. . . .

Again the watchers saw a smile pass across the sensitive mouth. . . . Once he awakened with the look of one who has returned from a far journey. He smiled, and raised his hand in a feeble blessing. Then again the weary eyes closed.

Why, he was only fifty years old, some of them were thinking—too young to die. It was little more than ten years since he had been ordained. Their minds staggered a little as they reflected upon all he had accomplished in those ten years. . . .

It was late afternoon, on the second of February, 1852—the Feast of the Purification of Our Lady. Off in the chapel, Vespers had begun. Dimly the chanting of the Magnificat came to those who were watching. *Et exaltavit humiles.* They saw that he had fallen asleep again. . . .

He was a child once more, and had drifted out to sea in a little boat—all alone. All was pleasant and lovely until suddenly the sky darkened and a great storm arose. His craft was tossed about by gigantic waves; at any moment he would perish. Then all at once he saw the ship with the great light bearing down upon him.

But this time he was not afraid. He rose up in the tossing boat and stood with his arms wide to welcome it. For he knew that in the midst of that light, there was a Man upon a

Cross. Nearer and nearer came the light. The sea quieted, and a star rose in the sky. And now the Figure, smiling as only God can smile, reached down and tenderly gathered up the son of the Rabbi of Saverne. . . .

The Star of Jacob was in the ascendant.